INDIANS

BLACK HAWK, *Cleven*
OSCEOLA, *Clark*
POCAHONTAS, *Seymour*
PONTIAC, *Peckham*
SACAGAWEA, *Seymour*
SEQUOYAH, *Snow*
SITTING BULL, *Stevenson*
SQUANTO, *Stevenson*
TECUMSEH, *Stevenson*

NAVAL HEROES

DAVID FARRAGUT, *Long*
GEORGE DEWEY, *Long*
JOHN PAUL JONES, *Snow*
MATTHEW CALBRAITH PERRY, *Scharbach*
OLIVER HAZARD PERRY, *Long*
RAPHAEL SEMMES, *Snow*
STEPHEN DECATUR, *Smith*

NOTED WIVES and MOTHERS

ABIGAIL ADAMS, *Wagoner*
DOLLY MADISON, *Monsell*
ELEANOR ROOSEVELT, *Weil*
JESSIE FREMONT, *Wagoner*
MARTHA WASHINGTON, *Wagoner*
MARY TODD LINCOLN, *Wilkie*
NANCY HANKS, *Stevenson*
RACHEL JACKSON, *Govan*

SCIENTISTS and INVENTORS

ABNER DOUBLEDAY, *Dunham*
ALBERT EINSTEIN, *Hammontree*
ALECK BELL, *Widdemer*
CYRUS McCORMICK, *Dobler*
ELI WHITNEY, *Snow*
ELIAS HOWE, *Corcoran*
ELIZABETH BLACKWELL, *Henry*
GAIL BORDEN, *Paradis*
GEORGE CARVER, *Stevenson*
GEORGE EASTMAN, *Henry*
GEORGE PULLMAN, *Myers*
GEORGE WESTINGHOUSE, *Dunham*
HENRY FORD, *Aird and Ruddiman*
JOHN AUDUBON, *Mason*
JOHN BURROUGHS, *Frisbee*
JOHN DEERE, *Bare*
JOHN FITCH, *Stevenson*
LEE DeFOREST, *Dobler*
LUTHER BURBANK, *Burt*
MARIA MITCHELL, *Melin*
ROBERT FULTON, *Henry*
ROBERT GODDARD, *Moore*

SAMU[...]
TOM [...]
WALT[...]
WILBU[...]
  Stev[...]
WILL [...]
  Ham[...]

SOCIAL and CIVIC LEADERS

BETSY ROSS, *Weil*
BOOKER T. WASHINGTON, *Stevenson*
CLARA BARTON, *Stevenson*
DAN BEARD, *Mason*
DOROTHEA DIX, *Melin*
FRANCES WILLARD, *Mason*
J. STERLING MORTON, *Moore*
JANE ADDAMS, *Wagoner*
JOHN PETER ZENGER, *Long*
JULIA WARD HOWE, *Wagoner*
JULIETTE LOW, *Higgins*
LILIUOKALANI, *Newman*
LUCRETIA MOTT, *Burnett*
MOLLY PITCHER, *Stevenson*
OLIVER WENDELL HOLMES, JR., *Dunham*
SUSAN ANTHONY, *Monsell*

SOLDIERS

ANTHONY WAYNE, *Stevenson*
BEDFORD FORREST, *Parks*
DAN MORGAN, *Bryant*
DOUGLAS MacARTHUR, *Long*
ETHAN ALLEN, *Winders*
FRANCIS MARION, *Steele*
GEORGE CUSTER, *Stevenson*
ISRAEL PUTNAM, *Stevenson*
JEB STUART, *Winders*
NATHANAEL GREENE, *Peckham*
ROBERT E. LEE, *Monsell*
SAM HOUSTON, *Stevenson*
TOM JACKSON, *Monsell*
U. S. GRANT, *Stevenson*
WILLIAM HENRY HARRISON, *Peckham*
ZACK TAYLOR, *Wilkie*

STATESMEN

ABE LINCOLN, *Stevenson*
ANDY JACKSON, *Stevenson*
DAN WEBSTER, *Smith*
FRANKLIN ROOSEVELT, *Weil*
HENRY CLAY, *Monsell*
HERBERT HOOVER, *Comfort*
JAMES MONROE, *Widdemer*
JEFF DAVIS, *de Grummond and Delaune*
JOHN F. KENNEDY, *Frisbee*
JOHN MARSHALL, *Monsell*
TEDDY ROOSEVELT, *Parks*
WOODROW WILSON, *Monsell*

Jane Addams

Little Lame Girl

Illustrated by Gray Morrow

Jane Addams

Little Lame Girl

By Jean Brown Wagoner

THE **BOBBS-MERRILL** COMPANY, INC.
A SUBSIDIARY OF HOWARD W. SAMS & CO., INC.
Publishers • INDIANAPOLIS • NEW YORK

Dedicated to my Father
Hilton U. Brown

The author gratefully acknowledges
the assistance of Mrs. Mary O'Haver
Ousley in procuring, firsthand, much
of the information related in the en-
suing pages. We are also indebted to
Mrs. Mary Henney-Smythe for personal records, to Mrs. Ida Jones Barber
for intimate recollection, and to Mrs.
Stella Perkins for photographs and de-
tailed pictures.

Illustrations

Numerous smaller illustrations

Contents

★ ★ ★

Books by Jean Brown Wagoner

ABIGAIL ADAMS: A GIRL OF COLONIAL DAYS
JANE ADDAMS: LITTLE LAME GIRL
JESSIE FREMONT: GIRL OF THE CAPITOL HILL
JULIA WARD HOWE: GIRL OF THE OLD NEW YORK
LOUISA ALCOTT: GIRL OF OLD BOSTON
MARTHA WASHINGTON: GIRL OF OLD VIRGINIA

★ Jane Addams

Little Lame Girl

Company at
the Addams'

LITTLE JANE ADDAMS was getting angrier and
angrier. It was her task each morning to sweep
the terrace at the front of the house. That's what
she was trying to do now, but it was a windy
day. As fast as she swept the pine needles and
sticks away, more fell.

Finally Jane threw the broom down and sat
on the front step and sulked. "I don't see the use
of sweeping. It's silly. Things get dirty right
away again," she thought.

Just then her father called to her from the
barn. "Do you want to go to Sparlings' with me,
Jennie? I am about ready to go."

11

Jane saw he had the wagon hitched up ready to go. "Yes! Yes! Wait for me!" she cried, in a good humor at once. She picked up the broom and ran around to the back of the house. "I'm going with Father," she called to Polly, the Addams' housekeeper.

Polly, a pleasant-looking old lady, came to the door. "Did you finish your sweeping, Jennie?"

"Yes, I'm all through," fibbed Jane, and ran to join her father.

For a little girl in 1865, a ride in the wagon with her father was a very special treat.

The wind grew stronger all day. By night it was a gale. The little town of Cedarville, Illinois, slept through the storm. Not a light shone from its windows. The wind swept down the main street and out to the edge of town.

It whistled around Mr. Addams' big house. It whined at the doors and pried at the shutters, then rushed on to the barn and spun the old weathercock till it was dizzy. It roared down the hill and across the road to the Addams' flour mill and on to the sawmill. It screamed through the lumber stacks.

Everything that belonged to Mr. Addams was snug and tight. The wind found nothing loose to rattle. No one even noticed it, except little Jane Addams.

Jane couldn't sleep. She wasn't sick, and didn't hurt any place in particular, but she was very unhappy. The fib she had told that morning bothered her. It hadn't seemed important in the daylight, for it was such a little fib, and she was only a little girl, five years old. Now, in the dark, though, it was different.

She listened to the wind and worried.

"I wish Father's room weren't so far away. I wish he were just across the hall where Mary and Martha and Alice are." They were Jane's older sisters.

Father's room was away downstairs. "If I didn't have to go past the front door, I wouldn't mind. That big old door scares me so."

She pulled the covers up over her head and tried to go to sleep. The wind howled in the pine trees outside her window. The harder Jane tried not to hear, the louder the wind cried. She worried and squirmed and tossed. Finally she got up. "I'm going to Father even if the goblins get me!" she said to herself.

She ran to the stairs and peered down into the dark. She couldn't see the front door, but she knew it was down there waiting for her. Drawing a deep breath, she flew down the stairs, past the front door, across the front room, and into her father's room.

"I told a lie this morning, Father."

Father woke with a start. "What? Who? Oh, it's you, Jane. What did you say?"

"I told a lie this morning," Jane repeated.

14

Father felt for Jane's cold little hands and said soberly, "Well, if I have a little girl that tells lies, I'm very glad she can't sleep until she has told me about it."

That was all he said, but Jane felt quite happy again. Father knew, and now everything was all right. She went back upstairs and wasn't at all afraid. She even looked back over her shoulder and stuck out her tongue at the big old door. "You can't hurt me," she bragged. "I'll just come back there and show you."

She thought better of it, however, and went to bed. The wind howled as loudly as ever, but Jane didn't hear it. She was asleep.

Mr. Addams didn't go to sleep right away. He thought about Jane. "She isn't like her sisters. They're well and strong. They like parties and dances and much company. Jane is quiet and plays alone.

"Sometimes she acts as if her back hurt. I won-

15

der if the fever she had when she was a baby made her that way. Her mother was so proud of Jane that crisp autumn day when she was born on September 6, 1860. We must take good care of her for Sarah's sake." Neither disturbing thoughts nor howling wind kept him awake long.

Knock! Knock! Knock! went the knocker on the Addam's front door the next morning.

"Who can that be?" said Polly, as she hurried to open the door. Polly was like a mother to Jane and her three sisters. She had lived with them all their lives and had taken care of them since their mother died three years ago.

"It must be a stranger," said Mary, the oldest sister. "Everyone else walks in without knocking." It was only at the Addams' house that people walked in. Almost everyone else kept their doors locked. It was not long after the War between the States and times were unsettled. Robbers and tramps were often seen on the roads.

16

Following Polly to the door, Jane hid behind Polly's full skirts. Jane peeked out to see who had knocked.

"It's a soldier!" she cried and ran back to tell her sisters. "He's taller than Father, but he's awfully thin." Just then Polly brought the soldier into the parlor.

"Why, it's Ben Thomas!" cried Mary when she saw him.

"So it is," said Polly, astonished. "I didn't recognize you without my spectacles, Ben. Now where did I put my specs?" she wondered, and began to look around the room for them. "They're not in my darning basket, nor with my Bible. What could I have done with them?"

Everybody began to hunt. All at once Jane pointed and said, "Why, Polly, they're on top of your head."

Sure enough, there they were on top of Polly's lace cap. "My goodness, it's a wonder I don't lose my head," she said. "It's a good thing I have you, Jennie." They all called Jane "Jennie."

"Now let's take a good look at you, young man," Polly said to Ben. "It's no wonder I didn't know you. You've grown a foot."

"I guess I am taller," Ben grinned. He had run away to be a drummer boy in the army when he was only twelve. Now he was seventeen.

"Have you seen your grandpa yet?" asked Polly thoughtfully.

"No, ma'am, I'm on my way to his place now. I've been in the hospital for ages. It's been a long way home," Ben replied.

Just then the front door opened and in walked several neighbors from nearby farms. They were all talking at once. They were used to seeing soldiers at Mr. Addams' place, so they did not notice Ben.

"The wind did a lot of damage in the country last night," said one farmer, Mr. Bell.

18

"It turned over the corn crib at Eastman's place," said another.

"Ripped the roof off the barn at Pepperman's, I hear," added Mr. Bell.

"It blew the chimney down at my place," said an old man. "That's why I came to see Mr. Addams. I need a man to help me set it up."

"How would I do?" asked Ben, and stepped in front of him.

The old man's mouth fell open. He looked up at the tall thin soldier. He blinked his eyes. "Why, you *can't* be Ben—but you *are* Ben," he cried and threw his arms around the young man. The old man was Ben's grandfather.

"My, won't Ma be happy!" he cried. "I've got a wagon outside. We'll whip up and get home as fast as we can."

"No, you won't," said Polly. "That young man hasn't had his breakfast. Nobody leaves this house hungry while my name is Polly Biers."

20

So Ben and his grandfather followed Polly to the kitchen. The other men sat down to wait for Mr. Addams. Jane ran to call her father. He was at the mill to see if the wind had torn anything loose.

"We have company, Father," she said, and told him who had come. Mr. Addams seemed almost as happy as Ben's grandfather and ran back to the house with Jane.

As they went up the drive, two little girls ran out of the house to meet them. "It's Cousin Mary and Cousin Lizzie!" exclaimed Jane. "When did you get here, Mary?" They were Uncle James's little girls, and Mary was the same age as Jane.

"I just now came, Jennie," said Mary, dancing around Jane and her father. "The wind blew a big tree down on our house. It tore a hole in the roof, and Lizzie and I get to stay here with you until it's mended."

21

"Oh, I hope it takes days and days," said Jane. "We can have such fun."

Jane's sisters were very good to her, but they were somewhat older than she was. They did not care to play little-girl games any more, so Jane was glad to have someone her own age to play with her.

"Come on, let's get started playing right now. We'll go over to the sawmill first."

The Dragon
in the Sawmill

MARY AND LIZZIE and Jane started down the hill
to the sawmill. There were some boys waiting
in the wagons in the yard. They were the sons
of the farmers who had come to see Mr. Addams.
Jane knew the boys.

"Don't you want to come along?" she asked.

"Aw, who wants to go with a bunch of girls?"
the boys said, though they really wanted to go.
They heard the saws whining away and could
hardly wait to see how they worked. Pretty soon
they trailed after the girls to the mill.

For a while they all stood and watched.

"Look at that pile of logs!" exclaimed one boy.

It'd be too bad if those logs slipped and all started rolling."

"They won't," said Jane. "The men know how to stack them."

"Watch 'em roll that log into place."

"What's that thing called that takes the log up to the saws, Jennie?" asked another boy.

"That's the log carriage," said Jane. "See how the saws cut off the bark and trim the log? The log carriage will take the log back and forth while the saws cut it into boards."

Soon Jane ran and climbed up on one of the logs as it moved along. The boys stared. The girls screamed, "Jennie! Jennie! Jump off! You'll be sawed in two." Jennie just waved at them and rode on the log clear up to the saws. Then she hopped off.

"Do it. It's fun," she told the boys. "Just jump off before you get too close." The boys couldn't move. Jane rode again and again.

"I pretend the mill's a big dragon," she told them. "It's talking. Hear it? It says in a low growly voice, 'Who's that crawling around on my dinner? I'm going to eat you up, eat you up.' Then it says in a high squeaky voice, 'Eat you up, eat you up n-o-w-w-w.' Then you'd better jump off quick. Just look at the saws eat up the lumber. Don't they make you think of a dragon's teeth?"

Jane's cousins thought they looked too much like a dragon's teeth. After a while, though, the boys saw how easy it was to hop off the log. The boys could not bear to let a little girl do something they could not do, so they climbed on the logs too. Soon both the boys and girls were all playing the dragon game and having lots of fun.

They were perched like chickadees on a log when all at once there was a terrible noise. *Whooo-eee!* it went, right in their ears. All of them fell off the log as if they had been shot. The foreman of the mill, whose name was Mr. Kent, doubled up with laughter at the sight. So did the other workmen. The mill had stopped.

"Oh, that was just the noon whistle," said Jane in disgust, getting up and brushing off her skirts. "You did that on purpose," she stormed at Mr. Kent. Then all the children had to laugh at what a sight they made sprawled on the floor.

The boys, of course, had to learn how to blow the whistle. They were tooting it away at a great rate, when they saw a strange procession headed toward the mill.

Tearing along the road from town came a swarm of people. They were as thick as bees around a beehive. A buzzing sound of many voices was in the air.

"What's going on?" the boys and girls wondered. "The whole town's headed this way."

They heard the clanging of a bell.

"Why, it's the new fire engine!" cried Jane.

"Hurrah! Isn't it a beauty?" yelled one boy.

Sure enough, out of the midst of the people flashed two big horses pulling the engine. Its fresh red paint and polished brass glittered in the sun. Steam hissed from the pumping engine. Sparks shot up out of the smokestack. The horses galloped. The engine jolted from one side of the road to the other. The firemen hung on to the sides for dear life.

This was the first fire engine pulled by horses that Cedarville had ever owned. The old one had been pulled by men, and the pump had been worked by men, too.

Some young men dashed up to the mill yelling at the top of their lungs, "Out of the way! Out of the way! Do you want the hose turned on you?"

The millworkers and the children stared at the men. "What's the matter with these men?" they thought. "We aren't in the way. We're standing up here 'way off the road."

Then to the astonishment of everyone inside the sawmill, the horses swung out of the road and headed for the sawmill.

"Where's the fire?" shouted Pete, the driver. Without waiting to hear, the firemen jumped down and began to unwind the hose. Two firemen grabbed one end of the hose and ran to the well. Two other men turned on the pumping machine that forced the water out of the well through the hose.

By this time—in only a few seconds—the other firemen had unhitched the horses and wheeled the engine in front of the mill.

"Here comes the water!" shouted the men with the hose, and handed the nozzle to Jake who was the captain. Jake pointed the hose right at the boys and girls. Out spurted the water, drenching every one of the them and scattering them in every direction.

"Hold on a minute, Jake," cried Mr. Kent, the

mill foreman. "The mill isn't on fire. What's the idea?" The men stopped the pump.

"What do you mean, it isn't on fire?" cried Jake in exasperation. "Everybody in town heard the alarm. I was sitting down to dinner when I heard the mill whistle. 'There goes the noon whistle,' I said to myself.

"Then it kept blowing and blowing. I jumped up from the table. 'That's the fire signal,' I called to my wife. 'The mill's on fire,' and I started on the run. By the time I got to the engine house, the other boys were ready to start."

While Jake was talking, more and more people came flocking to the mill. "Where's the fire?" they wanted to know. "I don't see any smoke. Why has the pumper stopped? What's the matter with the engine? Won't it work? Is the fire already out?"

"There isn't any fire," yelled Mr. Kent. "It was a mistake. I was just showing these boys how to blow the whistle. I didn't think about the whistle making the fire signal."

"Oh, pshaw!" said Jake and sat down hard. He meant to sit on a log, but missed and sat on the ground instead. He was too tired to get up, so he leaned his back against the log and mopped his forehead.

"Well, anyway," said one of the men, "we had a good practice run and beat our record. Mr. Addams says so."

"What's that?" asked Jake, looking more cheerful at the news of the record.

"That's right," spoke up Pete. "Mr. Addams says he looked at his watch to see if it was right by the noon whistle. Then he kept count of the time to see how long it took to get here and hook up the hose and everything. We beat our best record by four minutes."

"Whoopee!" shouted Jake, leaping into the air. The word of the new record ran through the crowd, and a great cheer went up. Men hoisted the firemen onto their shoulders. They called on Mr. Addams for a speech.

"He's the man that made us get a new engine," they cried. "He's the one that helped buy it. Speech, Mr. Addams, make us a speech!"

Mr. Addams stepped up on a log and said, "It's too bad Jake had to leave his dinner, and a lot of dinners are getting cold. I know, too, we're all glad to find out that the new engine works. Three cheers for Jake and all the men!"

Then the people cheered. The men tossed their hats, and the women waved their bonnets.

"It's like a Fourth of July celebration or something," said one. "I haven't seen so many of my neighbors since the meetinghouse burned down years ago."

"It takes a good fire to bring people out," laughed another.

Soon, though, the women remembered their

dinners spoiling on the stove. The men remembered their appetites, and everyone began to hurry home.

Ding! Dong! Ding! Dong! went another bell. This time it was the Addams' dinner bell. Away flew the children! Polly met them at the front step when she saw their wet clothes.

"Go right around to the back door," she said. "I don't want you to track up the front hall. What do you mean standing around outdoors in that wind? You'll all catch your death of cold." The children scampered around to the back door where Polly let them in and handed them towels to dry their hands and faces.

They were ready to sit down at the table in a jiffy and ate so much that Polly said, "I'm glad you aren't sprayed by a fire hose every day."

After lunch the boys went back to the sawmill, but they didn't blow the whistle any more. They knew all they needed to know about that.

Tea for the Governor

JANE HAD more dolls than any little girl in Cedarville. Some of the dolls weren't like any other girl's dolls. They were made of rolls of cloth with a ribbon tied tightly around the middle.

"The satin and silk and velvet ones are fine ladies," she explained to her cousins. "The calico and gingham and cotton ones are housemaids and cooks. Some of them are mothers in house dresses. Sometimes I wrap the best ones in rags and pretend they are princesses like Snow White or Sleeping Beauty."

Her doll furniture was small blocks of wood from the lumberyard. They were all shapes and sizes. Jane used them as chairs or beds or stoves or thrones or whatever she needed.

The girls were playing with the cloth dolls on the stairway one afternoon. They liked to play there so that the princesses could walk up and down the palace steps. That day Polly had other plans for the girls, at least she spoiled the plan the girls had for themselves.

"You'll have to move your things, Jennie," she said. "These steps have to be wiped down, and with the house full of company someone's going to fall over your furniture."

"All right," said Jane, gathering up her jumble. "Come on, Mary and Lizzie, we'll go play house at the flour mill."

"They won't let us play there," said Mary. "They'll tell us we're in the way over there, too."

"No, they won't. Mr. Ferdinand lets me play there all the time."

"Who's Mr. Ferdinand?" asked Lizzie.

"He's the miller. He's old and pretends to be cross, but he's my best friend."

It was dim and cool inside the flour mill. Mary and Lizzie couldn't see very well at first. They heard the water racing under the mill wheel, and they heard Jennie talking, but couldn't see her.

"The playhouse is in here," she was saying. Then they saw the big bins where the grain was kept. Out of one of the bins came Jane. "These empty bins are for us. See what nice rooms they make? This is my parlor, and back here is my kitchen. Won't you come in and visit? See the tables and chairs Mr. Ferdinand made me?"

Mr. Ferdinand had laid boards across blocks of wood for benches. The men had brought a log from the sawmill and had stood it on end. Jane used it as a table.

"Won't you sit down and have a cup of tea?" she asked. Her plates were flat pieces of bark. The cups were pine knots.

"If I had known you were coming," she said, acting grown-up, "I'd have made some cup-cakes for you. Oh, let's make some now."

The other looked about to see what they could use. There wasn't any mud or sand in the mill. They had never made their pies and cakes of anything else. On the floor were only piles of bran and coarse flour.

"Here are aprons and caps," called Jane, taking flour sacks from pegs in the wall. "Here are buckets, too. We have to get water from the mill-race." She scooped up water in her pail and emptied it on a little pile of bran.

"See what nice dough this makes when it's wet?" she said. She began to shape some in her hands. "I have lids and cups I use for pans for making pies and cakes."

Soon the girls had rows of pies and cakes turned out on a nice, wide board.

"We'll set them here in the door to bake in the

sun," said Jane. "Now let's clean house, and then we'll have a party."

They were busily sweeping and moving their furniture around when they heard voices outside. "It's Father!" cried Jane. "He'll come to our party."

"No, he won't," said Lizzie. "There's a strange man with him."

Jane ran to see who it was. "It's the Governor. He's nice. He's been to our house before. He'll stay to tea all right."

Father came into the mill. He didn't see the board full of goodies on the doorstep and nearly set his foot down in the middle of a two-layer "chocolate cake."

"Oh, oh!" he cried. "Watch your step there, Governor, or you won't get any welcome. If I'm not mistaken, Jennie's been baking."

The Governor laughed and carefully walked around the board.

39

"Is anybody home?" called Father.

"Yes, indeed," said Jane primly. "Will you stop for a cup of tea and a piece of my apple-sauce cake?"

"Ah!" said the Governor. "I thought I smelled something good."

Jane showed them into her parlor. "Be sure to wipe your feet," she warned them. "We have just finished cleaning house."

The Governor and Father were careful not to track up the floor, and didn't spill any crumbs when Jane passed the "cake."

"This is the best food I've tasted since I've been Governor."

Jane was so pleased she hoped her guest could stay for another piece.

"We have to hurry away this time," said Father, "but we'll be glad to come again."

After the men had gone, the girls washed the tea-things and put them away. They hardly had

40

straightened up when Mr. Ferdinand called, "Time to shut up the mill and go home."

"It seems as if we'd just started," sighed Mary.

"That's always the way," said Lizzie.

"We can start in again tomorrow where we leave off," said Jane. "Mr. Ferdinand doesn't let anybody touch my things."

"You have everything that anyone ever wanted in the world," said Mary enviously.

New Friends

JANE SAT on the hill in front of her house and watched Mary and Lizzie and three neighbor boys play "horse and buggy."

Two of the boys marched out in front. They were the horses. The third boy walked in back of them. He was the coachman. The girls were fine ladies taking a drive.

The coachman was wonderful. He wore a coachman's high hat and long-tailed coat and carried a whip. The hat was too large and fell over his ears now and then. The coat dragged in the dust behind him, but the whip was just right. There was nothing wrong with that. He guided the horses with a harness of string. The horses were bent with their make-believe load.

The girls walked behind their coachman, but pretended they were riding in an open carriage. They wore long skirts with trains and elegant bonnets that tied under their chins with long ribbons. They carried fancy lace parasols. Every now and then they bowed and smiled at Jane in a gracious manner.

This remarkable team paraded up and down the road. The coachman cracked his whip. The horses pranced. Suddenly they pretended to run away. What shrieking there was then!

"Whoa! Whoa!" yelled the coachman.

"Help! Help!" cried the ladies.

Polly and Mr. Addams were in the house. They heard the racket and looked out to see what was going on. They smiled at the sight.

"Why isn't Jane playing?" asked Mr. Addams when he saw her sitting on the bank.

"She said she would rather watch," said Polly.

"That's queer," said Father. "Doesn't she ever romp with the other children?"

"Not often," replied Polly sadly. "She says it hurts her back to play hard. Have you noticed how thin and pale she is lately? I think there's something the matter with her." Polly was near to tears. "There's something else that worries me about her. She holds her head over to one side a

44

little. She's getting pigeon-toed, too." Polly threw her apron over her head and began to cry. "I'm afraid she's going to be a cripple."

"There, there, Polly!" comforted Mr. Addams. "It may not be as bad as you think. She'll probably outgrow those things. Just watch over her. Please don't say anything about these problems to Jane or anybody."

The days flew by, and the cousins had to go home. The house seemed empty after they had gone. Jane was lonely. She felt even more lonely one afternoon because her old friend Mr. Ferdinand, the miller, was going away. He was leaving Cedarville, Illinois.

"I'm getting old," he told Mr. Addams. "The business is growing fast. You need a younger man here now. I'm going back to Pennsylvania to live with my daughter."

Jane watched Mr. Ferdinand climb into the wagon loaded with all his belongings. She sat in the rope swing in the front yard and waved to him as long as she could see him. She swung as high as the swing could go so she could see far down the road over the hill.

"I wonder what the new miller will be like," Jane said.

Father had told her that his name was Jones and that he had four children.

"I hope that some of them are girls and that they like me," she said to herself.

Polly saw Jane swinging all by herself, and called to her. "What are you thinking about, Jennie?"

"About the Jones children. Do you think they will say I am stuck-up if I don't run and jump and climb up on the barn roof?"

"Land sakes, no," said Polly, "and don't you let me catch you up there."

"Some children don't like you if you don't play that way," said Jane, "and I do want them

46

to like me. I'm so afraid they won't like nice, quiet games."

"Don't you want them to come?"

"Sometimes I do, and sometimes I don't," answered Jane.

At the very same time that Jane was worrying about the Jones children, a wagon piled high with furniture was coming into Cedarville. Perched on a sofa in the back end were the four Jones children—Alice, Frank, Ida, and Susie. Alice and Frank were older than Jane. Ida was the same age as Jane, and Susie was younger.

"What do you think Mr. Addams' little girl will be like?" asked Alice Jones.

"I thought there were four Addams' children, the same as there are of us," said Frank.

"Only one of them is little. The rest are grown up," Mr. Jones explained.

"I'll bet she's stuck-up because her father's so rich," said Alice.

47

"How rich is he?" asked Ida.

"He owns a lot of mills and two banks and a railroad, and I don't know what else." Frank sounded envious.

"My goodness, he's as rich as the whole world! No wonder she's stuck-up. I'd be stuck-up, too."

"I didn't say she was stuck-up. I said, I'll bet she is," Alice protested.

"It's the same thing," said Ida.

"It is not," argued Alice.

"What are you children arguing about?" called Mrs. Jones from the front seat.

No one answered for a minute. Alice was sure her mother wouldn't like what they had been saying. "Is Mr. Addams very rich?" she asked after a while.

"That's none of our business," said Mrs. Jones. "He is a good man. Every one trusts him and looks up to him. That's what counts."

"What's his little girl like?"

48

"I don't know, but I knew her mother. Mrs. Addams was the kindest woman I ever knew. She was always doing good."

"Where is Mrs. Addams now?"

"She died. Her nurse takes care of the house and the children."

"Is the nurse kind to the little girl?"

"I suppose so."

"I guess I'll be kind to her, too. I didn't know she didn't have a mother."

"That makes it different," said Ida. "No matter how rich she is, I feel sorry for her."

"Mr. Addams will be a wonderful man to work for," said Mr. Jones. "He's one of the best millers in the country. I like to work for a man who knows his business."

"Cedarville isn't a very big town," said Frank. He was disappointed.

"It may not a big town, but it's a good one," said Mr. Jones. "There are no poor people in it."

"Here's the flour mill," cried Mother, "and there's our house just beyond it."

All four children jumped up to get a first look at their new home. Over went the sofa, and all four of the children spilled out into the road.

Mr. Jones stopped the wagon, jumped to the ground, and ran around helping them up.

Mr. Addams and Jane were standing at their gate waiting for the Jones family. They saw the sofa tip over. Father was beside Mr. Jones in one jump. Jane came at a hop, skip, and jump.

"Oh dear, I hope you're not hurt," Jane said to Ida, the little girl about her own size.

"I'm not hurt at all," said the little girl, "but I'm afraid I lost my combs, and they were brand new. They were just like yours."

"I'm sure we can find them," said Jane and helped her look for them. They searched under the wagon and in the weeds at the side of the road, and finally found all of them.

50

Ida was so happy she hugged Jane and said, "I hope you live near here. My name's Ida, and I'm going to live in the house next to the mill. My father is the new miller for Mr. Addams. I wish you were Mr. Addams' little girl."

"I am," answered Jane shyly. "I'm Jane Addams. My friends call me Jennie."

"Oh, Jennie," cried Ida, "I know I'm just going to love you."

At these kind words Jane forgot she had ever been afraid to meet the Jones children. She found out their names and how old they were. "This is going to be fun, having friends," she thought.

Father seemed to think the same thing. "You must come to our house to eat until you are settled," he said to Mrs. Jones.

"Oh, we couldn't think of it," she answered, though she wanted to very much. It was so hard to unpack and move in and cook at the same time. "There are too many of us," she went on.

"Who says there are too many?" asked a pleasant voice, and there was Polly. She had seen Jane's happy face and knew that the Jones family was all right.

"You will come to dinner right now," she said. "Don't try to unpack a thing until after you've eaten. Jennie, run and tell Joe to come look after Mr. Jones's horses." Joe was the man who took care of Mr. Addams' horses and cows.

Jane and Ida went to find Joe, then they came back and went through the Joneses' new house. By that time Polly was ringing the dinner bell. Jane proudly brought her new friends home.

Little Chefs

THE JONES family were soon settled in their house across the way. Jane was over there almost as much as she was at her own home. The girls had many good times together.

Then one day Jane came home looking very glum. "What's the matter, Jane?" asked her sister Alice. "You look as if you had lost your last friend."

Jane didn't answer.

"Maybe the cat's got her tongue," said Polly.

Finally Jane said, "Mr. Jones is mean."

"Why, Jennie, how can you say such a thing?" He has been so good to you."

"He won't let us play in the flour mill any more. He said, 'You children must move your things out of the mill now. You have two big yards to play in. Don't play around here any.'" Jane began to cry. "It was the very nicest place to play that ever was."

Polly said, "This is a pretty howdy-do, I must say. A little girl can't play in her own father's mill. We'll see about that." And she went straight for Father's study.

But Jane ran after her and caught her skirts. "Father already knows about it, Polly. He says that Mr. Jones is right. So many more people are bringing their wheat to the mill that the bins are overflowing. There isn't room for us."

"Well, that's different," said Polly.

"Mr. Jones is really nice," said Jane. "I was just angry."

"I'm glad to hear you say so," said Polly. "But now what we are going to do for a playhouse for you? I know! Call the two Alices to come help me. I'll make you the kind of house I had when I was a girl."

She went outdoors and took the clothesline from the post. There were four trees close together in the front yard. She fastened one end of the clothesline about one tree, then wound it around the others, back and forth, and across.

"While I'm doing this, you two Alices go up to the attic and get the big pile of cotton blankets that are in the linen chest," Polly directed. "Jennie, go over and get Ida and your dolls. We'll have a house here in no time."

The two Alices brought the blankets, and Polly spread some over the lines to make a roof and hung some close together to make walls.

By that time Jane and Ida had come, loaded down. They had their dolls, their doll cradle, a little red rocking chair, and a three-legged stool. The girls took their toys under the blankets.

55

"Oh, Polly," Jane cried, "this is much prettier than the house at the flour mill. It's so light in here. The grass is like a fine carpet. Come in and see us," she urged.

"We'll have a tea party for you, Polly, just as soon as we've put our children to bed," said Ida.

Just then there was a loud clap of thunder. Polly looked up in astonishment. "My goodness me! There's a storm blowing up. Quick, children, run into the house! You mustn't stay here under the trees when there's lightning."

The wind began to bend the treetops. It jerked the blankets off the lines and sailed them across the yard into a cherry tree. Polly ran after them. The rain came down in torrents. Poor Polly was soaked when she reached the porch.

"Serves me right," she said. "Anybody would think I had more sense than to play dolls in the rain. I hope Mrs. Jones didn't see me. She will think I'm crazy."

Mrs. Jones did see her. "I think Polly Biers is one of the sweetest ladies that ever lived," she said to her husband. "I don't know what she's doing running around in the rain, but you know it's something for the children."

"It is fine for our children to have such good neighbors," said Mr. Jones. "I'd like to do something special to please little Jane. I had to tell her to stay away from the mills. She really isn't ever in the way. But she plays that dragon game, and it's dangerous."

"Yes, and she isn't strong," Mrs. Jones agreed. "She might be badly hurt jumping from a log."

"Mr. Addams and I both thought she had better stay away, but I know she misses her playhouse. Can you think of something she wants very much?" Mr. Jones asked.

Mrs. Jones thought a minute. "I think I know the very thing," she said. "It will take a little time and some planning, but I'm sure you can do it."

58

"What is it?"

"Let's give the children a little stove, a real one, one they can cook on."

The idea of a stove was given proper attention, but Mr. and Mrs. Jones didn't tell anyone of their plans.

"I wonder why Jennie is so late coming to dinner," said Polly one day. Everybody was ready and waiting to sit down at the table. "I rang the bell several minutes ago."

"Where is she?" asked Mr. Addams.

"At the Joneses', of course," answered Polly.

"Isn't she over there too much? Aren't you afraid she'll wear out her welcome?"

"You don't need to worry about that. People don't get tired of Jane. Mrs. Jones sent for her herself this morning."

"I'd better go after her," said Mr. Addams.

"I'll go," said Mary.

"I'll go," said Alice.

"You'd all stay too long," said Father, smiling. "Serve the soup, Polly. I'll be right back with her." He hurried out the door.

Half an hour later Polly set her lace cap straight and marched out of the Addams' front door. "There's something going on over at the Joneses' house," she said, "and it's high time I found out what it is."

She had waited ten minutes for Mr. Addams to came back with Jane. He didn't come, so she sent Mary after him to see what kept him so long. Ten minutes after that she sent Alice. Now she was going herself to see what was keeping all of them at the Joneses'.

Before she could knock at Mrs. Jones's door, it flew open. There stood Jane. Her cheeks were fiery red. Her eyes sparkled. On her head was a chef's cap, and she wore a white apron.

"Oh, Polly! Come out to the kitchen and see what's there," she cried, and flew ahead of Polly.

60

"You just won't be able to believe it. I thought I was dreaming when I saw it. Best of all, it really works!"

By that time they had reached the kitchen. There stood a little stove. It was exactly like the fine new range at the Addams' house, except that it was just the right height for Jane and Ida. It had its own smoke pipe and damper. The stove lids lifted off, just as on a big stove.

"Look!" cried Jane, delighted at Polly's amazement. "We have our own pots and pans and kettles and dishes." She showed her a little corner cupboard with its shelves full of shining small pots and pans and a set of blue dishes.

Mr. Addams and Mr. Jones sat at the kitchen table. They looked satisfied and very happy. "We have just had a fine dinner," they said. "Our little girls are true millers' daughters. They know how to cook and bake. We had pancakes that they mixed and fried themselves."

"So this is why my own dinner sits over there getting cold!" said Polly. "Well, little ladies, how about giving me some pancakes, too?"

"Of course we will!" they cried. "Sit down." Then Ida and Jane proudly served Polly at the kitchen table. Mrs. Jones and all the others had had theirs earlier.

This was the first meal that Jane and Ida cooked, but it was not the last. They learned to be the best cooks around Cedarville.

"Jane is just a natural-born cook," Mrs. Jones said proudly.

"I do believe she will be famous for it some-day," Polly agreed.

A Playhouse of Her Own

WHAT'S ALL that pounding?" asked Polly one morning. She was making jelly and couldn't leave the kitchen. "Suppose you run and see what it is, Jennie. It seems to come from out in front."

Jane ran to the front of the house and saw Father and Mr. Kent out in the yard. Mr. Kent was hammering a stake into the ground. Father was measuring off a space. "Put the next stake here, Mr. Kent," he was saying.

He looked up and saw Jane. "Come here, Jennie. Can you guess what Mr. Kent's doing?"

Jane saw four stakes in the ground in a square. "Is he going to make a flower bed here?" she asked. "It's not a very good place, is it, because it doesn't get enough sun?"

"What do you think of it as a place for a little house?" asked Mr. Kent.

Jane held her breath. She was so afraid he might be teasing. "A little house," she said to herself. "Could he possibly mean a playhouse?"

She looked at the space marked off by the stakes. It was just the size she would love a house to be. She hoped they weren't teasing.

"Mr. Kent and the men at the mill saw what the rain did to the house Polly made you the other day," said Father. "They were sorry to see your doll cradle and chairs out in the weather. They're going to build you a real house."

"You must tell us just how you want it," said Mr. Kent. Tell us how many windows and doors, how high, what color you want it painted, and everything. We'll make it just as you say."

Jane couldn't believe her ears. "Mr. Kent, this

is better than the little stove, even. I must run and tell Ida. We'll have to make plans."

Two happy little girls were busy all morning with pencil and paper. They drew pictures of their house from all sides. Some were of the front with a door in the middle, and some with a door at one side.

The girls asked many questions. "Will the windows really open? Will they have glass in them? Will the door have a latch?"

They drew an outline of the house on the ground and walked around in it. Then they decided where they would put the cradle and the rocking chair.

"This will have much more room than the bin did," said Jane. "There will be a corner for another chair. If we had a table, it could go in the middle. There's plenty of room for us to walk around a big table."

Polly was nearly as excited as the girls were.

"We must get curtain material in town," she said. "I'll make curtains for the windows, and I'll show you how to make rag rugs for the floor. I am sure you can."

Jane took the plans to Mr. Kent, and he and the men went to work on them. The next day a load of lumber came in the drive. A carpenter came with it and started building the house.

Jane couldn't eat that day. She was too excited. Polly brought her a sandwich and let her eat it out on the lumber pile. Ida came over and joined her. They brought out their dolls and set them where they could watch, too.

"At night," said Jane, "when everybody is asleep, they can talk about the house."

"They'll get to sleep in it when it's finished, too. Sometimes I wish I were a doll," said Ida. "Then I could sleep out here."

While the carpenter sawed and hammered and painted the house, the girls braided rugs.

Finally the house was finished, inside and out. Mr. Kent looked it all over, then he locked the door and brought the key to Jane.

"Your little home is ready for you, Jennie," he announced. "Here's the key."

Jane and Ida opened the door together. "It smells so nice," said Jane.

"It's the dearest little house that ever was," said Ida happily.

The girls could stand on a chair and stretch their arms up and still not touch the ceiling. The windows opened and shut. The door had a latch. There was a front doorstep, and the front window had a window box. The house was painted white with green shutters. It had a roof of green shingles.

After they had run in and out, opened the windows and locked and unlocked the door, they moved in. Ida hung the pretty white ruffled curtains Polly had made. Jane put down their bright rag rugs. Then together the girls carried in the furniture, the cradle, and chairs.

Jane was wishing that they had a table, when she heard a knock at the door. There was Mr. Kent with a little table he had made for her. Soon two of the men from the mill brought over chairs they had made to match the table. There just couldn't have been two happier girls!

Mrs. Jones brought red geranium plants and set them in the window box.

That afternoon Jane and Ida gave a tea party for everybody who had helped with the house. They served cookies they had made on their own little stove, and they used their blue dishes.

"I don't suppose we'll ever be able to get the children to come home at mealtime again," said Polly jokingly.

"But we'll always know where they are," said Mrs. Jones, laughing contentedly.

The girls played in their house day in and day

68

out. They cleaned, swept, dusted and set things to rights. The boys liked the new house, too, but they played a different game with it.

They liked to pretend that the house was a log cabin in the woods and that there were Indians all around. Some of them were Indian chiefs on the warpath, and some were scouts. When the boys played, there was a lot of shooting and whooping and yelling. It was so exciting sometimes that Polly brought out cookies and lemonade to quiet things down.

On days when Jane was tired, Polly sent the boys away. One morning Eli Bennethum and Eugene Bucher were disappointed because they couldn't play Indian.

"What can we do to get even?" Gene asked as they walked away through the woods. "We've got to tease Jane and Ida some way."

"We don't want to do anything to make Polly mad at us," said Eli, "but those sissy girls don't deserve that nice house. They just play dolls in it all the time."

"Yeah, sissies," said Gene. He was swishing a stick through the bushes. A big green worm was crawling along a twig and was knocked off by the stick. It flew through the air and landed at their feet. Gene was about to step on it, but Eli stopped him.

"Hey!" he said. "Don't step on that worm. That's just the thing we want."

"Sure enough," agreed Gene, delighted. "We'll throw it in the window at the girls. I can just hear Jane yell."

Gene and Eli put the worm on a plantain leaf and carried it with them to the Addams' yard. Hiding behind bushes, they crept up behind the playhouse. Gene crawled along the wall till he was under one of the windows. Then he rose and, yelling like a Comanche Indian, threw the worm in the window.

He saw it land on the table right under Jane's nose. In a flash he and Eli dashed for the woods.

A great screeching and yelling began inside the house. Out ran Ida, screaming at the top of her lungs. Both boys ran after her. "Here's another one, Ida. Look! Don't you want one down your neck, Ida?"

Poor Ida ran for Polly. The boys looked back to see why Jane didn't come out. They wanted to chase her, too. There wasn't a sound inside the house. That scared them. "Gee, you don't suppose she fainted, do you?"

They didn't know whether to run away and hide from Polly or to go and call her. They peeked in the window to see what had happened. There was Jane leaning over the table. She was poking the worm gently and watching it. The boys nearly fainted with surprise.

Jane glanced up and saw them. "Where did you get this worm?" she asked eagerly. "It's pretty, isn't it? Come and look at it. Did you see the colors on the underside?"

It had never occurred to the boys to notice what the worm looked like. It was big and fat and good for scaring girls. That was all they had thought of.

Jane showed them how it was striped with beautiful colors. "Take me where you found it," she said. "Maybe we can find out what it likes to eat. We'll get some of the leaves."

"How about keeping it in the little house?" asked Gene. "Maybe it would make a cocoon."

"And we'd see what kind of a moth came out," added Eli.

"I bet it'd be a beauty," said Jane. They went back to the place in the woods where Eugene and Eli had found the worm, and cut off some branches. Then they started back home, making plans all the way.

Polly was waiting for them at the door of the

little house. She was angry, for she was worried. Ida thought the boys were still chasing Jane.

"I told you boys you were to let the girls alone," Polly said crossly. "I won't have you scalping them or chasing them with snakes."

"They weren't bothering us, Polly," said Jane. "We're playing science. See the lovely moth?"

Polly didn't see any moth. She saw a big, ugly worm. She wouldn't touch it with a ten-foot pole, she said. But she saw that Jane was happy, so she let the boys help Jane put the worm in its new home in the playhouse.

Ida didn't like it much, but she got used to it for Jane's sake.

After that whenever one of the boys found a new bug or worm, he brought it to Jane.

"I used to think Jane was afraid of her own shadow," said Eugene one day, "but she isn't afraid of anything."

A Trip
to Freeport

JANE AND IDA sat on the doorstep of their little house and watched the birds that flew past above the treetops.

"They're flying south for the winter," said Ida. "We'll be starting to school next week. I can hardly wait."

Jane didn't feel quite that way about it. She wished the summer could go on forever. She wanted to go to school, but was afraid, too. Jane didn't feel like a big six-year-old girl. "It scares me to think of being with all those strange boys and girls."

"Why, that's funny," said Ida. "You already

know many of them. Your sister Alice and my sister Alice will be there. You aren't afraid of them. You know Frank and Gene Bucher and Eli Bennethum and Anna Bell's brother and Alma Richardson's brother."

"I know," said Jane miserably, "but I'm afraid anyhow. I shiver inside when I think of it."

The week flew by. School opened. The Cedarville school was built on top of a hill. Forest trees grew behind it, but the front slope was bare. It was fine for coasting in winter.

Jane liked school, even though she felt shy with so many people around. Her teacher, Agnes Bennethum, was pretty and young, almost as pretty as Sister Alice, Jane thought.

The children sat on benches. Jane found them hard. "Doesn't your back get tired?" she asked Ida one day.

"Of course, but I go get a drink out of the water bucket in the corner. That gives me a chance to stretch my legs. Why don't you get up and walk around?"

"I feel as if everybody were looking at me," said Jane.

"What if they are? I don't see how you can sit so still."

Jane was too bashful to follow Ida's example. She sat as quiet as a mouse, until her back hurt so badly she'd almost cry.

Miss Bennethum seemed to know how tiresome it was to sit still. She brought little red chairs to the schoolroom. When it was time for the first readers to recite, she let them sit in the red chairs in a circle around her. That helped Jane's back some, but not very much.

One morning Jane's back seemed worse than usual. Her legs felt numb. Miss Bennethum called for the primary class to come up front. Jane was afraid to move. The others started, and she felt silly sitting back alone. She knew they'd all look at her and wonder, so she tried to stand up even though her legs felt numb.

A terrible thing happened. Jane fell and hit her back on the edge of the bench. It hurt so badly she forgot what people would think. She cried out loud.

Alice Addams was in a classroom upstairs.

She heard someone running up the steps. The door flew open, and Ida ran in. "Alice, Alice, come quick! Jennie's hurt, and the principal wants you to get your father."

Alice stopped just long enough to run in and squeeze Jane's hand and tell her that Father would be there soon. Then she started on the run. Halfway down the school hill big Gene Bucher caught up with her. Alice couldn't believe her eyes. Gene was crying.

"I'll get Mr. Addams," he said. "I can run lots faster than you. You go stay with Jennie," and he was off like a shot.

It happened that Mr. Addams was coming from the blacksmith's. He was riding his favorite horse, Prince. Gene met him at the foot of the hill and told him what had happened.

Father galloped up the hill and reached Jane almost as soon as Alice did. Then Alice mounted Prince and went for the doctor, while Father carried Jane home in his arms. She was so little and thin, she felt as light as a feather.

Polly saw Mr. Addams coming and held open the front door. By that time Jane was smiling. "Don't be scared, Polly. It doesn't hurt any more. I could really walk."

But Polly and Father weren't so sure. When the doctor came he wasn't sure, either. "I don't know whether she will ever walk again or not," he whispered to Mr. Addams, after Jane was in bed asleep. "As soon as she can stand the trip, you must take her to the doctor in Freeport. In the meantime—no more school."

Jane surprised everybody. In a few days, she was up, walking and running around as if nothing had happened. She didn't go back to school, though. Father taught her at home.

It was fun having lessons at home with Father. Jane learned so fast she was soon far ahead of the other children. She could read long before Ida could, and Ida didn't miss a day of school.

"I wish I were as smart as you are," said Ida one day.

"But you are," said Jane.

"No, I'm not. You can read and write, and even say the Lord's Prayer in Latin. I can't do any of those things."

"You can do something else, though. You can speak a piece in front of the whole school. That's something that I'd be afraid to do."

Soon after, the fall rains came. From her window Jane watched the trees grow bare. It was gray, cold, and miserable outside.

"I think I'll pretend I'm sick this morning and stay in bed today," said Jane to herself one morning. "Maybe Polly will bring me biscuit and blackberry jelly and hot chocolate for breakfast. First, I'll see what it's like outdoors. I'd hate to stay in bed if it happens to be nice."

She tiptoed to the window and pushed the shutter open a crack. Cold air rushed in on her bare feet. A light snow was falling. "Ooo-ooo! It's colder than ever." She was about to pop back into bed when she heard Father's voice. He was out on the front steps calling to Mr. Jones.

"I won't be at the mill this morning," he was saying. "Jane and I are going to the city. We may be gone all day."

"Going to the city!" cried Jane. This certainly was *not* the kind of day to stay in bed. She fairly jumped into her clothes, but when it came to lacing up her shoes, she had trouble. One of the laces was frayed at the end and wouldn't go

81

through the hole. She wet it and twisted it and tried to get it through, but it bunched up each time and stuck.

"You mean old thing!" she cried, and yanked off the shoe. "You do that just because you know it hurts my back to bend over so," and she threw it across the room. "I'm going to hurt you and see how you like it." She ran and jumped up and down on it. Then she stubbed her toe and went hopping about on one foot.

"Jennie, is that you making all that noise?" called Alice from the stairs. "Hurry down to breakfast. Father has already finished his and gone to the barn to hitch up Prince. You're going in the new buggy."

"In the new buggy!" shouted Jane. "Oh my!" She hadn't ridden in the new buggy. Father had just driven home in it the week before. It had been made at the Henney Carriage Works in Cedarville. Jane and Ida and Alma had watched

the men make it. Alma's father was the post-
master, and the family lived above the post office.
The girls could look out of Alma's windows onto
the carriage factory. There, without being in the
way, they could watch the men working.

The new buggy had seemed to sparkle in the
sun. It was a beautiful glossy black trimmed
with a narrow yellow stripe. Even the spokes of
the wheels were finished that way. Now Jane was
going to Freeport in this elegant carriage.

She took up her shoe again. "I'll give you just
one more chance," she said. "I suppose you can't
help it if your laces are no good." This time the
lace slipped through as if by magic. "Why didn't
you do that in the first place?" she scolded. "See
all the trouble you got into by being stubborn.
Now we must hurry."

Polly let Jane eat her breakfast in front of the
fire in the kitchen. "It's much warmer here than
in the dining room. Your wraps are on the rack

in front of the living-room fire. I want them to be good and warm before you put them on— You're not eating enough," she fretted. "Try to eat a little of the ham or some scrambled eggs."

But Jane was too excited to eat, and it was just as well. Father was at the door with the buggy before she had finished her chocolate. Jane hopped up from the table.

Polly bustled about bringing heavy blankets and carriage robes. She buttoned Jane's coat up tight. "Now be sure to keep your mittens on and keep your hands in your muff."

Father lifted Jane onto the seat beside him and tucked the covers around her. He set a box under her feet, for her legs were too short for her feet to touch the floor. Then he lifted the reins ready to start their ride.

"Wait, wait!" called Polly. "We forgot the bricks." Out she came with two bricks wrapped in cloth. They had lain close to the fire all night

and were hot through and through. Father put
one under Jane's feet and one under his.

"Thanks, Polly," he said. "These will keep our
feet warm all the way to Freeport."

Then he lifted the reins again. This time there
was nothing to stop them. Off they went, whirl-
ing out of the drive in a flurry of snow.

"There go Mr. Addams and Jane," people cried as the little girl and her father whizzed through Cedarville. Jane waved and shouted as long as anybody was in sight. She forgot all about keeping her hands in her muff.

"Don't your hands ever get cold?" she asked her father as she put hers inside again.

"No, my hands are old and tough."

Jane watched her father's hands. "How strong they are!" she thought. "I wish my hands were like his, but most of all I wish my thumb looked like his." Mr. Addams' thumb on his right hand was broad and flat.

"Tell me how your thumb got like that," she coaxed him.

Father smiled. "You already know all about it. I have told you many times."

"But I want to hear it again. Begin at the first, when you were a boy."

"In Pennsylvania," began Father, "where I

came from, the boys begin to learn a trade almost as soon as they start to school. My uncle was a miller. I thought I would like that trade, so I worked for him."

"How much money did he pay you?"

"I didn't get any money. He gave me food and a place to stay. That was all anyone was paid while he was learning," Father explained.

"Did you have to work very hard?" Jane already knew, but she liked to hear again.

"I had to go to work every morning at three o'clock. I had to have everything ready: the fires hot, the mill spick and span, the bins cleaned out. I worked till suppertime. I did this for so long that I still wake up at three."

"But that isn't why your thumb is so flat."

"No, that came from rubbing the wheat between my thumb and fingers. Every miller has a thumb like that."

"How long did it take it to get that way?"

"Several years, I guess."

"I've been trying a long, long time, ever since I was little, to make mine like that. It hasn't changed a bit," sighed Jane. "Look." She held up her hand for her father to see.

He studied her thumb. "Now, how old are you?" he asked.

"Just past six! Do you think it will ever get flat? I rub wheat that way every day."

"I don't believe I'd worry about it," said Father finally. "Maybe when you grow up you'll be a schoolteacher or a wonderful cook like your mother. A big thumb would be in the way."

Jane didn't say anything more, but she thought to herself, "I still want a thumb like Father's. I want to be exactly like him."

All the rest of the way Jane kept her father busy telling her stories about when he was a boy. Long before she was tired, they came to Freeport. It was a happy journey.

Jane loved Freeport. Everyone was so friendly. When they stopped at the Pennsylvania House, the stableboy ran out to hold the horse. Mr. Mayer, the owner, came out to welcome them. People on the street bowed and smiled.

The first thing Father and Jane did today was to go to see the doctor. Jane liked him. He was jolly and kind. While he talked to Father, he let Jane play with his big Angora cat.

After they left the doctor's, Father went to the bank. Jane went to William Walton's store. That was her favorite store, because Mr. Walton always saved samples of his finest cloth for her. He knew she used them for her dolls.

Sometimes there were pieces from New York and London and Paris. He knew the names of some of the great ladies who wore dresses of these materials. He told her about them and the balls that were given for them.

Jane did not have time to visit as long as usual

today. "I have to stop at the old mill I used to own here," Father said, "so we'll have to start home early."

Mr. Walton wrapped up the beautiful bits of satin and silk for Jane. He helped her into the carriage as if she were one of the elegant ladies herself. Jane was having a very good time.

Father left the city by a different road this time. They didn't go down the wide street with the big shade trees and fine homes with lovely gardens and lawns. They went down the narrowest, dirtiest streets Jane had ever seen.

"Why, Father, these people haven't any yards at all. There isn't any room for the children to play. Why did the people build such little houses so close together?"

"They haven't enough money to buy bigger houses or yards. They have to live where they can walk to work, too."

Jane stared at the ugly houses and streets and

the children who played in the dirt because there was no grass.

"When I grow up, Father, I shall have a big house, a great big house, but I won't have it where all the other big houses are. I'll have it right in the middle of these little houses. Then I'll let all the children come and play in my yard and my house."

She was so full of her plans, she didn't notice her father's sad face. Father had bad news to take home. The doctor had said, "Jane's back is crooked, and there's nothing that I can do to straighten it. It was the fever she had when she was two years old that did it. Her back will always hurt. She'll always be pigeon-toed, and her head will be twisted to one side."

No wonder Father's eyes were filled with tears. His little Jane would never be rosy and strong like her sisters and cousins. All the money in the world could not buy her a straight back.

Father didn't stop at the old mill long. Soon they were on their way again. Before they reached Cedarville, Jane had forgotten the poor houses and dingy streets. Her mind was filled with other thoughts.

"With all these new make-believe dolls I'll have a grand ball like those they have in Paris. I'll make the red velvet one a queen with a long train." She showed the pieces to Father and told him the wonderful plans she had in her head.

Her dreams made Father smile again. "No one can be sad near Jane," he thought. "Even a crooked back won't make any difference."

Jane woke the next morning feeling cross and grumpy. "There was some reason why I didn't want this day to come," she thought. "What was it? Oh, now I remember. Alice is going away to boarding school."

All summer and winter Alice had been getting ready. Two seamstresses had come and sewed for days making dresses and coats and hemming sheets and pillow slips. It had been exciting packing things and hearing the talk of her older sisters and Alice's friends about the good times at boarding school.

Now that the day had come for Alice to go, Jane felt so lonely she could hardly keep from crying. Mary, her oldest sister, was through school and was away visiting. Martha, the next sister, had left for school the week before. Now with Alice going there would not be anybody left but Polly and Father. Jane would rather be with Father than with anybody, but he was away much of the time.

"Maybe I won't feel so bad if I help pack the last things," she thought. She heard Alice and Polly hurrying back and forth across the hall, so she dressed and joined them.

When she went into Alice's room, there was the big trunk wide open, and piles of dresses, petticoats, hats, books and linens stacked on the bed and chairs and on the floor. Alice was nearly standing on her head. She was lifting things out of the bottom of the trunk.

"Why, Alice," cried Jane, "what are you doing? It will soon be time for Joe to come for the trunk." Joe was going to load Alice's trunk in a cart and take it to Freeport where it would be put on the train. "You can't get half of this back in. It took us all fall to pack it."

"Joe isn't coming for the trunk, Jennie," replied Alice quietly.

"When is he coming?" asked Jane.

"Not this year."

"Has Father lost his money?"

"No, no," said Alice. "I'm just not going to school this year. I'm staying home with you."

Jane danced and skipped around the room singing. "Alice isn't going! Alice isn't going!" She threw her arms around her sister. "I do hope you don't mind too much, but I'm so glad you're staying home. It is terrible to think of being here without you."

Jane's happy face made Alice glad. She had felt a little sorry for herself all morning, because she had wanted to go away to school so badly. But last night when Father told her about Jane's back, Alice had come straight upstairs and started unpacking her trunk.

"Jane will need me," she had said. "I can't have fun away at school and know that Jane is lonely and miserable."

That winter Jane and Alice did everything together. Alice was beautiful and gay and kind. She had many friends and all of them were good to Jane. When there was snow, the boys came every afternoon to take Jane and Alice to the toboggan slide on the school hill. They carried Jane piggy-back to and from the hill, and saw that she had as many rides as she wanted.

There were dances, too, and no one had more partners than little Jane. Sometimes the tall boys held onto her by her hair ribbons, saying they couldn't reach her hands.

It should have been a wonderful winter, but something happened that spoiled everything for a long time.

The Dreadful Sunday

IT HAPPENED one Sunday. Jane loved Sunday. Father was home then and that meant good talks and stories. She always walked to Sunday school with him. It made her happy to look up at this fine, tall man and know that she belonged to him.

This Sunday as they walked along some boys and girls came up behind them. Jane heard them giggling and turned around to see what was making them laugh. One of the boys was following right behind her. He held his head way over to one side and was stumbling along pigeon-toed and knock-kneed, and the others were laughing as if they thought he was the funniest thing in the world.

When the boy saw Jane looking at him, he turned red and ran away. But she knew what he had been doing. He had been making fun of her, imitating the way she walked.

"Do I look like that?" she wondered.

She knew she couldn't hold her head straight. She had known that for a long time, but she had thought that no one else noticed it. She looked down at her feet. They *did* point in.

She wanted to run home and hide, but what could she tell Father? He hadn't seen the boy and didn't know that anything was wrong. He kept walking toward the church, and so Jane tagged unhappily along.

Father taught the Sunday school lesson that morning. Usually Jane hardly breathed for fear she would miss a single word. Today she was so unhappy that she didn't hear anything he said.

All she could think about was the way that boy mocked her.

"Does everyone make fun of me behind my back?" she wondered. The more she thought about it the more miserable she felt.

Soon Sunday school was over. People were getting ready to go home. There were twice as many there as usual. It was always that way when Father talked. She could see him now in the center of a crowd of people. All of them wanted to shake his hand. How wonderful he was!

"I'll slip out and go home alone," she thought. "I wouldn't want these strangers to know that my father has a funny-looking, crippled daughter." She started home, then stopped. "If people see me alone, someone may point at me and ask, 'Whose little lame girl is that?' Then someone else will answer, 'That's Mr. Addams' little girl. Isn't it too bad such a fine-looking man has such a queer-looking child?'"

She saw her uncle James a little way ahead of her and caught up with him.

Uncle James was fond of Jane. "Is there anything wrong?" he asked when he saw her sad little face.

"Oh, no," said Jane, and walked as straight as she could, because she was afraid even Uncle James might be ashamed to be seen with her.

As soon as she got home, she ran up to Alice's room where there was a long mirror, and looked at herself. "I'm ugly. My hair isn't pretty like Alice's. My face is white, and my eyes are too big." She turned around to see how her feet looked from behind.

It hurt her to turn her head so far. It, also, made her back seem a lot more crooked than it was, but Jane didn't think of that.

"I look just like that boy," she cried. "Oh, I wish I had never been born!" She ran into her room and crawled into bed.

"No one can see my feet here," she said, "and no one will notice my twisted back. I'm never going to get up again."

All day she stayed there. No one could find out what was wrong. Polly brought up her favorite dessert, but Jane could not swallow it. There was such a lump in her throat nothing could get past it.

Father sat beside her all afternoon and read to her. Alice scooped up a handful of snow from her window sill and made a snowball for her. The boys called to her to come out and play, but nothing could bring a smile to Jane's face.

Night came and everyone went to bed. Then Jane began to think. "I feel the same as if I had told a lie. I don't hurt and I'm not sick, but when I stay in bed everybody thinks I am. It makes me ashamed to be so much trouble, and it isn't any fun, either.

"I'll get up tomorrow. All the folks around

here know what I look like anyway. They're used to me. I just won't go where there are any strangers." Then she fell asleep.

She was up early the next morning and ran out to the kitchen. Polly and Joe were there arguing. Joe was saying, "It's bitter cold out and I just want to bring them up here for a few days."

"Bring what up here?" asked Jane.

Polly hadn't know before that Jane was there, but she was so bothered with what Joe was saying, she forgot to be surprised to see Jane up and dressed.

"The cat that stays at the barn has kittens," said Joe, "and I wa——"

"Let me see them, let me see them!" cried Jane, jumping up and down.

"I don't think you can get to the barn," said Joe doubtfully. "There's a hard wind out. Polly, I'll just bring 'em up and put them back of the stove out of the way."

102

"Indeed you will not," said Polly. "I'm not going to have a houseful of cats under my feet."

"They can't even get out of their box yet," protested Joe. "How can they get under your feet if they are so little?"

"I'll keep them in the wardrobe in my room," suggested Jane eagerly.

"A fine thing that would be!" snorted Polly. "Cat hairs all over your good clothes!" But when she saw Jane's disappointed face she changed her tone. "Well, you can bring up one pussy, Joe. But mind, Jane, you can only keep it a little while. It's too young to stay away from its mother for very long."

When Joe brought the tiny kitten to Jane, she was so excited she forgot all about the trouble of the day before. She had seen a lot of kittens, but none as small as this one.

"Why, Joe," she cried, "it hasn't any eyes."

"Oh yes, it has. It just hasn't opened them yet.

103

It'll be a few days before it can see. Just keep it warm, and don't squeeze it too tight. I'll be back when it's time to take it to its mother."

Jane found a shoe box and lined it with some of her velvet pieces to make a nice, soft bed for the kitty, and took it into the front room. She sat close to the fire and laid her cheek on the kitten's soft fur. When Polly called her to breakfast, Jane set the box on the hearth.

She ate as fast as she could and hurried back, but it was not very soon because she was hungrier than usual. What she saw in the box when she came back made her cry out in surprise. She clapped her hand over her mouth so that Polly wouldn't hear her. In the box was the mother cat and three more kittens. Jane wanted to whoop, but she kept perfectly quiet.

"Did Joe bring you in here?" she asked the mother cat in a whisper. "Or did you miss your baby and come to find it? You wanted all your babies to be in this nice, warm place, didn't you? I won't let them take you back to that old cold barn, but I'll have to hide you because Polly won't like it."

She tried to lift the box, but the mother cat was so big some of the kittens spilled out. That worried the mother cat terribly. Jane put the kittens in, left the mother out, and started upstairs with the box. The big cat meowed so loud, Jane was afraid someone would hear her. Finally, she put all the cats back in the box, left it on the hearth, and tiptoed up to Alice's room.

Alice was still asleep, but Jane woke her. "I need you quickly," she said. "Don't dress. Come down to the living room and help me."

Alice didn't know what to think when she saw Jane up and well, but she was so glad that she didn't ask any questions. She threw a shawl around her shoulders and followed her downstairs. When she saw the kittens she nearly let out a shout, too, but stopped herself in time. She helped Jane carry the cat and her family and the box upstairs and hide them in the wardrobe.

Jane and Alice kept their secret for three days.

It was the mother cat that gave them away. She was so proud of her kittens that she led Polly up to Jane's room and showed the kittens to her. Polly laughed and thought they were so cute that she didn't tell Jane and Alice that she knew anything about the kittens.

She let Jane keep them for three whole weeks. By that time the kittens were tumbling all over the room. Jane had to be careful where she stepped in the mornings. One little kitten learned to catch hold of the counterpane and climb up on the bed. It would hide behind a lump in the covers. If Jane wiggled a finger, the kitten would pounce on her finger like a tiger.

Finally Polly said they would have to get the cats out of the house. "Why don't you take the kittens around the neighborhood and see if you can't find homes for them when they're ready to leave their mother?"

Jane was so anxious to get her pets settled that

she forgot her resolution not to go where there were strangers. She went from house to house with her basket of kittens. All the people thought they were so pretty that no one seemed to notice Jane was pigeon-toed.

Jane forgot all about it herself. She didn't think about her back except when it hurt too much or when she saw herself in the big mirror. "It's silly to lie in bed and hide," she told herself. "I can walk and run and do all the things that anybody else can do. It's selfish to ask people to wait on me."

A New Coat

THERE WAS only one place that Jane wouldn't go, and that was to Sunday school.

"Why don't you go with Father any more?" asked Alice. "That used to be the happiest part of the week for you. See how lonely he looks going down the street without you."

Jane felt guilty. "I just can't bear to have them make fun of me."

"Who makes fun of you?"

"The boys and girls at Sunday school. They laugh at the way I walk." Then Jane told Alice all about that awful Sunday.

Alice was so angry at the children that she said

109

she'd like to punch their noses. "I'll paddle that boy right in front of his friends and see how funny he thinks it is to have people laugh at him," she cried.

It was Jane's turn to laugh. The thought of her pretty sister Alice turning a boy over her knee at Sunday school was too much for her.

"I know what we'll do," said Alice. "You've always worn my old dresses, and they don't look right on you. We'll buy you some pretty clothes. The next time you go to Sunday school you'll look so much nicer than any of the other girls, they'll be sorry they ever laughed at you.

"When Father goes to Freeport, we'll go with him. We'll pick out the prettiest cloth Mr. Walton has. Then we'll stop to see Mary Graham, the dressmaker, and ask her to come over and make the things as soon as she possibly can."

Mr. Walton had an extra fine piece of coat material. Mrs. Graham sewed day and night to get

110

the coat finished by the next Sunday. Every time Jane tried it on she felt happier.

"Now, Jane," said Alice, "you must practice walking in front of the mirror. You're not nearly as pigeon-toed as you think you are. Besides, it's all right if your head is tilted over a little to one side. You look interesting. Now walk straight up to the mirror, and you'll see."

Jane did as she was told. Sure enough, she didn't stumble at all. "When you are thinking about your feet, you fall all over yourself," said Alice cheerfully. "Anyone does that."

Jane could hardly wait for Sunday morning.

It finally came. When she was ready to go, Alice whispered in her ear, "Now, think about your coat and not about your feet. You'll walk as straight and be as pretty as anybody."

Father was waiting for her when she ran downstairs. He smiled happily to see her so gay. But when he looked at the coat he stopped smiling. "Jane, you aren't going to wear that coat to Sunday school, are you?" he asked thoughtfully.

"Why yes," answered Jane faintly, "don't you like it?"

"Yes indeed, I think it's a beautiful coat. It's the most beautiful coat I ever saw. That's just the trouble. No other little girl in Cedarville could afford anything half as nice. Won't it make the others feel bad? After all, your old coat is perfectly good and just as warm."

Jane took the coat back upstairs and brought out the old one and put it on. It seemed uglier than ever, and it seemed to her that her feet were bigger and clumsier than before. She walked along beside her father scuffing the ends of her shoes on the gravel walk, and kicking little stones out of her way angrily.

"What do I care if I do make the other children feel bad? They made me feel bad, didn't they? I can't help it if their fathers don't make as

112

much money as mine." On and on went her thoughts, and she felt sorrier for herself every step of the way. At the church door she stopped her father.

"Father, how does it help anybody for me to wear my old coat? That doesn't make the poor children have any more money. There are always some people poorer than others."

"Yes, Jane," said Father, "I suppose there will always be some people poorer than others. But at church we think about things that are more important than clothes and money. We remember that we are all children of the same Father, and that we are all equal before Him. Then isn't it too bad to wear things to church that make it hard for some people to remember that?"

Jane thought a minute. Then she grinned. "I was thinking of my coat, wasn't I, and how I could get even, and not about church at all?" Then she put her hand into her father's to show

him that she was sorry. She didn't stumble, and
they went happily into church together.

One morning not long after that, Father
called Jane very early. "Would you like to go

with me? I'm going after Alice." Alice had been visiting friends near Freeport for a few days.

Jane wanted to go, of course, so she flew around to be ready by the time Father brought the carriage to the house. She was in such a hurry that she put on her old coat, forgetting she had a new one. They were nearly at Freeport before she thought about it.

"Oh dear," she said to herself, "here I am in my old coat, and Father has on his Sunday coat and high silk hat. I'm so afraid he'll be ashamed of me. I do hope he doesn't stop in Freeport."

But he did.

"You can visit at Walton's or the candy shop, or wherever you wish," he said. "I have to go to the bank, but I won't be long."

Jane bought some bonbons for Alice and then started for Walton's. She had to pass the bank, which was on the busiest corner of the city. As she went by, she thought, "I wish I were straight and tall like Father. Then if he met me on the street he would bow and all the people would look at us and say, 'See how proud Mr. Addams is of his pretty daughter Jane!'"

Just then the door of the bank opened, and out stepped Father. People all about bowed and spoke, but Father didn't see them. He saw little Jane, and he smiled and swept off his hat and bowed to her as if she were the loveliest lady in the land. Jane smiled so happily at her father that one woman said to another, "Mr. Addams is a lucky man to have such a loving daughter."

Jane didn't hear her. She was thinking, "I'm glad now that I wore my old coat! Now I know Father likes *me*. He didn't even notice what coat I had on. He bowed just the same here in the city with all these strangers around as if we were at home. I'll never, never think about my pigeon toes or my twisted back again. They don't count. I've been silly."

116

George, Snakes, and Caves

TIME PASSED. Jane was eight years old. Alice had gone to boarding school. Jane was still at home, but she wasn't alone. Father had married again, and Jane had two stepbrothers, Harry and George.

Harry was a little older than Alice, and he was studying in Europe. George was the same age as Jane. She liked him the minute she saw him, but he wasn't so sure about Jane. He wished she had been a boy, but he thought for a girl she was all right.

"We could do more things if you were a boy," he said. "We could go walnut hunting."

"I can go walnut hunting," said Jane. "I know where the best trees are, too. We can hitch up old Tom to the wagon, and take a lot of gunny sacks, and get all the nuts we want."

"Say, that's an idea," said George. "I'll tell some of the other boys. They'll probably want to go, too."

Off he went while Jane found Joe and asked him to hitch up old Tom. She was in the wagon waiting when George came back with three boys. They were arguing.

One of them, whose name was Bill, was saying, "No old girl is going along on a nut hunt with me, especially one like Jane."

Jane heard him. She knew he didn't want her to go because she wasn't strong.

"I'll stay home, George. I don't mind," Jane spoke up quickly.

George said, "It's Jane's horse and wagon. If she wants to go, she can go, I say."

118

"She'll get too tired and want to come home," said another boy, named Dick.

"And somebody will have to carry her sack for her, too," added Bill.

"Sometimes we have to carry them a long way, and they get awfully heavy," put in Dick.

"I'll carry my own sack," said Jane.

"Besides, it's dangerous," said Bill. "One time we were gathering nuts in a field where there was a bull, and we didn't see him. He came charging down on us. We dropped our sacks and ran as hard as we could. We barely got away. He nearly caught Dick. We waited and waited for the bull to go away so we could get our nuts."

"But he didn't go away," finished Dick, "and we had to come home without any."

"Well, all we have to do," said Jane, "is to look and see if there's a bull around before we go into a field."

"Aw, we might as well let her come," said

Dick. "But don't blame us if you get hurt," he added darkly. "Come on, we're losing too much time arguing."

The other agreed, so they all piled into the wagon. George slapped the reins on old Tom's back, and they set off at a slow trot.

As they drove along, the boys told George of all kinds of narrow escapes that they had had while hunting walnuts. They watched Jane out of the corners of their eyes to see if she were frightened.

Jane didn't pay any attention to the boys. By the time they came to the walnut grove, they had scared themselves more than Jane.

George drove the wagon up close to the fence. Everyone looked over the field to see if there were any bulls or mean cows. They couldn't see a sign of anything that might hurt them. The children left the wagon by the side of the road, took their sacks, and climbed the fence.

The ground was covered with nuts and soon their bags were full. Jane filled hers to the brim and then found that she couldn't budge it. She tugged and pushed, but had to give up. She wouldn't call one of the boys to help her, so she emptied half the nuts onto the ground, carried the rest to the wagon, and came back for more. The boys were dragging their full bags over the ground and were about halfway to the fence, when George let out a shout.

"Look what's coming! Run!" They all dropped their sacks and started on the run. They didn't stop to look. They could hear what was coming after them. It was a dog, and his fierce barking scared the wits out of them.

The boys didn't stop running till they reached the fence, and they skimmed over it as if it weren't there. It wasn't until they were safe on the other side that they thought of Jane. George turned white with fright when he looked back.

121

Jane had been the farthest away, and she couldn't run as fast as the boys. The dog was close upon her. They all saw that she couldn't make it to safety. Jane saw it, too.

She knew that the boys were too far away to help her, so she turned toward the dog. His ugly snarling face was awful to see. Instead of screaming with fright, she said in a cheerful, coaxing voice, "Here, doggie, nice doggie!"

The dog started wagging its tail so hard it nearly threw him end over end. He came up to Jane and licked her hands and face, and jumped all over her, and seemed to say, "I'm so glad you knew I was only fooling." Jane gave him a friendly pat and picked up her sack of nuts.

The boys felt pretty sheepish. They climbed back over the fence to get their sacks, but the dog started growling again as soon as they came near. He drove the boys back and wouldn't let them leave the fence.

"Call him off, Jane, so we can get our nuts," begged Bill. Jane called the dog and tried to hold him, but she wasn't strong enough. In the end, Jane had to drag all the sacks to the fence. She managed it slowly by making two trips to a sack. The boys poured the nuts into the wagon, and Jane would go back for more.

The dog walked along beside her while she went back and forth, as if to say, "I'll see that those bad fellows don't hurt you." She finally had gathered up all the nuts and told the dog good-by. He stood at the fence and whined and cried after her as long as the wagon was in sight.

From that day on, George was Jane's best friend. They spent many hours together.

Jane didn't have much time for dolls after George came. There were too many other exciting things to do. George liked to go exploring. Wherever George went, Jane followed.

One day they were walking along the millstream. The bank rose steep and rocky on each side. George had gone a little way ahead. All at once he shouted, "Jennie, come here! Hurry!" She ran to catch up with him. "Look! I've found a cave!"

"What about it?" asked Jane, not seeming at all excited.

"What about it!" shouted George. "Do you mean you've known about this cave all the time and didn't tell me?"

"Why, of course. There are a lot more of them farther along," Jane answered.

"Why didn't you tell me? Have you already explored all of them?" George asked.

"Oh, no. Ida and I weren't allowed to play this far from the house. I've never been in them at all, but I would like to go exploring."

"Then come on," cried George. "Let's go through them now. First, though, we must each have a big club. These are probably robber caves. We may have to fight robbers and pirates, you understand."

He cut a big, stout stick for Jane and another for himself. Then they went into the cave.

The opening was small and the two children had to crawl in on their hands and knees, but, inside, the cave was bigger. They could stand up.

"What makes it so cold in here?" whispered Jane with a quavering voice.

"Because the sun never shines in," answered George. "Why are you whispering?"

"I don't want the robbers to hear me." Jane was really scared by this time.

"There won't be any robbers in this cave. It's too little. Are the other caves bigger than this one?" George asked hopefully.

"I don't know. Some of them are just big enough for one person to sit in, but I think there's one that's bigger."

"Let's go farther on, then."

126

George and Jane found many more caves. They tried to count them, but soon lost track.

"We'd better make a map," said George "We'll mark down each cave and name it."

Jane was pretty tired by this time. They had been climbing up and down the banks and over rocks and fallen logs.

"I'll rest on this rock a minute," she said. "Then we'll go home and get some paper and pencils to make our map."

"And some candles," added George.

"What do we want candles for?"

"One of these caves is going to be really big. It's bound to be. Then we'll have to have candles to see where we're going."

Jane had climbed up on the rock and was just going to stretch out, when George yelled, "Don't move, Jane! There's a snake!"

Jane didn't move a muscle. She looked down. The snake was just under her hand.

"It's a copperhead," whispered George. "Don't move your hand until I'm ready to strike. I'll count to three. When I say 'three,' jerk your hand away."

George crept to the rock and raised his club. "One—two—three," he counted. Down came the club! Jane slipped her hand out of the way in the nick of time. *Whang! Biff! Bang!* George's club whaled away at the snake and killed it.

"That was a poisonous snake," said George. "They're dangerous. We're going to have to be careful. Do you know a poisonous snake from a harmless one?"

Jane didn't. She thought all snakes were bad.

"Oh, no," said George. "Some do a lot of good. I'll have to teach you which are which. Then you'll have to kill the bad ones." He thought Jane would be scared at this, but she wasn't. She wasn't afraid to study the copperhead George had killed.

"I'll know this kind if I see it again," she said. "Tell me about some of the others."

By this time they could see by the sun that it was past noon. So they hurried home to lunch.

They were so late that Mrs. Addams wouldn't let them go back that afternoon. Besides, she saw that Jane needed to rest.

But the next day they went again. They did find a big cave. It was so big they really needed their candles. They couldn't see a thing without them. Exploring became a real adventure.

They went far back in the cave when Jane whispered, "George, do you hear something?"

"Yes," he whispered back. "What do you think it is?"

"It sounds like someone talking, or pigeons cooing," Jane replied.

They searched the whole cave. George held his club ready to strike if they found a robber or something dangerous. But they didn't find anything. They could hear the noise, but they couldn't find what made it.

"It's getting late again, and we'll have to give up for today," said George. "Mother won't let us come any more if we're always late to lunch. We'll find out what it is sometime."

They stopped at the big, flat rock on the way home. This time there wasn't any snake on it. They sat there and worked on their map a few minutes. They marked each cave carefully.

"We'll call the big cave the Mystery Cave. We ought to name this rock, too," said George.

"This will be the Altar Rock," said Jane.

"That's a good name," said George, "and we'll bring every snake we kill here, because this is where we found the first one."

"Let's bring any treasure we find here, too," added Jane.

"Yes, sir! That's just what we'll do."

All summer they played along the stream and

in the meadows. Jane grew stronger than she had ever been. She learned the different kinds of snakes, and could kill the dangerous ones as quickly as George could. She thought them so pretty that he showed her how to dry the skins and make belts out of them.

The first time Jane wore a snake belt up to the house Polly admired it. But when she found out what the belt was made of, she shrieked. "Take it off and throw it back in the creek where it belongs," she cried.

"It doesn't belong there any more," replied Jane. "Look at it and feel it. It's nice."

"I can't bear to touch it." Polly shuddered. "Don't bring any of those things in the house again, please."

So Jane and George kept most of such treasures down at the Altar Rock.

At the End of the Rainbow

ONE RAINY day there was a lot of hustle and bustle at the Addams' house. There was going to be a big dinner party. A lot of important people were coming.

This dinner was not to be like the parties they had had before Jane's stepmother came. It was to be much more stylish. Joe was to have two helpers to take care of the horses and carriages of the company. Polly wasn't to see to the cooking. Always before she had cooked the dinner, and all the Addams children had helped. Often a neighbor came in to help serve.

That big day a chef came from Chicago to

prepare the dinner, and he brought his own help with him. There was to be a butler at the door. Jane and George were not to eat with the grown-ups. They were to have their dinner in the upstairs living room. That suited them. They were told to stay out of the kitchen.

"Half the fun of a party is tasting things," said Jane.

"And smelling them," added George. "I can't even get near the pantry to sniff at the good things. Let's take a lunch down to the Altar Rock. If it begins to rain hard, we can stay inside one of the caves."

Mrs. Addams thought that a good plan. She let Polly pack a basket for them, and off they went. Ida and Susie and Frank went with them. Jane and George spent the morning showing them the map and the caves and their treasures.

They saved the Mystery Cave to the last. It began to rain hard just as they reached it, so they lighted their candles and ate their lunch inside the big cave.

"No wonder you call this the Mystery Cave," said Frank in a low voice. "It's spooky in here with all the shadows dancing around us and with that funny noise underneath."

"Underneath?" asked Jane and George together. "We didn't think of that. We've been trying to find where that noise came from."

"Maybe that's where the robbers hid their treasure. I expect there's a dragon guarding it, and he's swishing his tail around under there," Ida said.

Susie was frightened when she heard this, and thought she had better go home. But George told her they were just pretending.

"Let's really find out today what makes the noise," he said. "First, we'll draw a map of the cave. Then we'll make a mark where the sound seems loudest."

134

They did this, and found that the noise went straight across the middle of the floor.

"Now what?" asked Frank.

"We'll go outside and walk around the cave and look at each end of this mark. Maybe we'll find a door leading down, or something."

Their eyes got big with excitement. The boys ran out, unmindful of the rain that still fell.

Jane and Ida and Susie stayed together as they went outside. All at once Jane put her ear to the ground and shouted, "I've found it! I've found it! Right here."

The boys came running. Jane pointed to a hole in the ground. A merry little stream that tumbled down the bank disappeared into the hole.

"I'll bet this little stream runs under the cave," said George.

"Maybe it comes out on the other side," suggested Jane excitedly.

They ran around to see. Sure enough, out from

135

a rock on the other side of the cave came the little stream.

"Drop a stick in it on the other side," said George. "I'll stay here and see if it comes out."

"I'll use the cork from the catchup bottle," said Jane. "A stick might get stuck."

She ran back and dropped the cork in the water. George and the others waited and waited. No cork came out. Jane came to watch, too.

"There it is! There it is!" and up popped the cork. They snatched it out of the water, and ran around and dropped it on the other side again, then raced back to watch it come up. They had so much fun they didn't realize how fast the time went.

The afternoon was nearly gone when they noticed that it had stopped raining. The sun came out, and across the sky they saw a gorgeous rainbow.

"Let's go to the top of the bank and see if we

can tell where the rainbow ends," cried George, running ahead of the others.

"I've never seen one as bright as this. It reaches clear to the ground!" exclaimed Jane.

"Do you know that story about the pot of gold at the end of the rainbow?" asked Susie.

"Of course we do," replied Frank. "Everybody knows that, but we know there really isn't any gold at the end of it."

"How do you know? Have you ever been there?" Susie asked.

"No, but I've heard stories about children trying to find it, and there isn't any," said Frank.

"Maybe they just weren't good at finding things," Jane said suddenly. "I'd like to try just once. It seems funny to me that people still talk about that pot of gold if there isn't any."

"This would be a good one to find out on," said George. "I can see right where this rainbow ends—right over that field."

"So can I!—So can I!" cried the others excitedly. "Let's go there as fast as we can." They started off at a run.

"We'll bring the pot right back here," panted Jane as they ran, "and pour a little of the gold on the Altar Rock."

"Yes, indeed," agreed George. "This'll be our first gold."

They raced across the wet meadows, through a shallow stream, and up a hill. On the top of the hill Father had planted some pine trees long ago. The rainbow ended in the middle of these trees.

They all had seen it. It had faded long before they reached the spot, but they kept on going because they knew exactly where to look.

But when they came to the spot, there wasn't a sign of anything like a pot of gold. George climbed the trees. The others hunted under every bush and low-hanging limb.

All at once George cried out in a queer voice, "Jane, come up here." She climbed as fast as she could. "Look!" he cried, and pointed toward the western sky.

"O-o-o-h!" cried Jane. The whole world was a golden color. The mist from the rain was like gold dust in the sun, and the rain drops sparkled like diamonds on the pine needles.

It was getting late. The sun was setting. Even

while they looked the gold began to fade. "Oh, George," sighed Jane, "if we could just carry a little of this kind of gold back to the rock!"

George looked very serious. "Jennie, I'll bet there some way to do it, if we just knew how. When we grow up we must study real hard, and maybe one of us will find out."

Then far off, they heard a bell ringing, ringing, ringing.

"That's Polly with the dinner bell," said Jane. "She wants us to come home and get cleaned up before any of the company comes. We'll have to hurry, or we'll be late."

They all joined hands and ran down the hill, through the shallow stream, across the wet meadows, home.

A Christmas Gift for Father

ANOTHER SUMMER passed. Jane was so much healthier she went to school again.

"It comes from playing outdoors all day with other children," said Mrs. Addams.

Polly looked up from her darning and smiled. "I know that has helped, but Jane will never be quite like other children."

"What do you mean?" asked Mrs. Addams.

"I don't know just what it is, but there's something about her that is different."

"Don't be silly, Polly. Jane is an unusually sweet girl, a little too quiet, maybe, but not too different from the other children."

"It isn't just that," insisted Polly. "She had a lot more courage than most children. She wouldn't be walking today, if she hadn't. And she's smart, too."

"Of course she is," agreed Mrs. Addams. "But she has one bad fault. She's too shy. She won't speak out in company at all."

"Someday, if there's something she really wants to say," said Polly, "Jennie will speak out to the whole world, and people will listen. Mark my word. She is only nine now, but she makes her place among the children. Someday she will make her place in the world."

Winter came. The snow lay in great drifts over the highways and against the houses. Joe shoveled with all his might to keep a path clear from the house to the barn. He put away the buggy and brought out the sleigh. Children got out their skates and sleds. The sound of sleigh bells filled the air.

"Christmas is just around the corner," said Polly briskly. "You must buy me some colored sugar at the candy shop, Jennie. I'll want to start on the Christmas cookies tomorrow."

"It won't be long before we go to the woods to pick out a tree for the church," said Jane, "and one for our house."

"Let's get a lot of pine branches to decorate with this year," said George, "and some mistletoe to hang over the door."

"Let's have a lot of candles too, one in every window and some on the mantel. There probably will be bayberry candles in the package from the Pennsylvania relatives. Oh, Christmas is the very nicest time in the whole year!" Jane said happily.

"What's the part you like best?" George asked Jane.

"I like it when you wake up Christmas morning and run down and see the stockings on the mantel. I love the smell of the tree, and the way it

sparkles in the firelight. What do you like best?"
Jane in turn asked George.

"I like Christmas Eve best, just when we're
going to the meeting at the church. I like to look
back and see our tree all shining, and the packages under it. Then I like the walk to the church
and the light from the windows on the snow."

"What part do you like best, Polly?"

"I like the church meeting. I love to hear the
children singing the carols at the Christmas
tree." There was a softness in Polly's voice.

"Oh, Polly, I wish you hadn't mentioned the
singing!" sighed Jane.

"Why, Jennie, that's the very loveliest part of
Christmas," Polly repeated.

All the joy had gone out of Jane's face. Her
heart was like a lump of lead. Polly tried to find
out what was wrong. Finally Jane told her. "Ida
Jones and Alice Carl and I are to sing a song at
the church Christmas Eve, just the three of us."

"Why, that's wonderful," said Mrs. Addams, who had just come in. "You have a sweet voice, and it will please your father to hear you."

"Oh, but I won't be able to do it." said Jane.

"Why not?" everybody asked.

"Because I just know I can't," said Jane. "Each of us has to sing a whole stanza all alone. Every time I try to sing by myself my throat gets so dry not a sound comes out. Oh dear, why did I say I would try to do it?"

"You're being selfish, Jane," said Mrs. Addams sharply. "You're not thinking of the pleasure you'd give your father. You're just thinking of your own little self. That's not like you at all."

Jane hung her head and didn't say anything more about it.

As Christmas drew near, she grew more and more miserable. Even wrapping the presents wasn't as much fun as usual. Ida and Alice came over and talked about the white dresses they were going to wear. They could hardly wait to put them on.

"Our teacher says we're to have tinsel in our hair. Won't it look sparkly in the candlelight?" Ida said, wishing to cheer Jane.

But Jane remained downcast. "Both of you will be able to sing. I'll stand there with my mouth open, not making a sound. I'll wish I could fall through the floor. Ida, you'll have to learn the words to my stanza. Then if I can't go on, you sing for me. Promise you will."

"If it will make you feel better, I will," said Ida. "But it will be much better if you just sing out and stop worrying."

A few days before Christmas Father said, "Jennie, can you spare tomorrow to go to Freeport with me? I have some shopping to do, and you're the only one who can help me." He handed her a list of names. "This is the list of the

146

Sunday school children, and I want to get every one of them a present. I'd like to be sure it's a present he wants more than anything else."

Jane was delighted. This was something she could do. She knew all the boys and girls, and she was pretty sure what they would like to have.

She and Father started out early the next morning. It was clear and frosty outside.

"It looks like a Christmas card outdoors, doesn't it?" cried Jane.

A fresh snow had fallen the night before. The houses were decorated with holly wreaths. Sleighs, with bells jingling, passed by. The streets were full of people laden with Christmas packages. "This is the way it always ought to be at Christmas time," said Jane.

Father was so jolly, and she was so happy to be able to help him, Jane forgot to fret about the singing. They had fun all day, talking over the list and deciding what to give everybody.

147

After they had bought the last present and were on the way home, Jane asked, "Now, Father, what would you like to have more than anything else for Christmas?"

"More than anything else, little Jennie, I'd like to see you happy, the way you are now."

"But, Father, that isn't a present."

"It's all I want," he said. "You know," he added after a while, "it isn't always easy to be happy. We have to work for it. Sometimes we have to do something that's awful hard before we're really happy.

In the night Jane remembered Father's words. "I'll sing my stanza at the church and be happy about it. That will be hard to do. I'll make it a kind of present to Father."

Christmas Eve came. The Addams house was bright with candles. The tree shone. The floor underneath it was piled high with presents. Everybody was ready to go to the meeting.

148

"Now we're having the part of Christmas that you like best," Jane said to George as they went out the door.

No one could talk on the way to church. The wind was so sharp it seemed to cut off their breath. It stung their cheeks. But the snow sparkled like diamonds in the light from the windows. Sleighs flashed by. There was excitement in the air.

The church was full. It seemed to Jane that the whole town was there. It was a long way to the front of the church where the tree stood, straight, tall and alight with candles.

The children began to sing the Christmas carols. Jane looked at Polly and smiled. "This is the part that Polly likes best," she said to herself. Her own heart began to pound. It would be her turn next. "What if no sound comes out when I start?" Her heart came up into her throat.

The carols ended. Ida and Alice were getting

up. Jane had no feeling in her legs at all. She felt as if she were walking in a dream. But the first thing she knew she was standing beside Ida and Alice, facing the congregation.

They began to sing. The three voices sounded weak and tiny to Jane. "Oh dear, this is awful," she thought. She saw her stepmother and George and Polly and her sisters. They all looked worried. "They know how frightened I am. Everybody must see it."

Then she saw Father and remembered. "It isn't always easy," he had said. She smiled at him. It was her turn to sing alone. She opened her mouth, and sang!

When the meeting was over the folks were on their way home, more than one person said, "I don't know why, but the part I liked best in the service was Jane Addams'. She doesn't have a big voice, and it wasn't much of a song, but there was something about her that was different."

150

The next morning Jane woke early. "Merry Christmas!" she called, and ran downstairs to get her stocking. Everything was just the way she loved it. The stockings were lumpy with presents. The tree sparkled. The pine branches smelled good. She was so happy she felt she would burst.

Father was standing beside the fireplace. She ran to him and kissed him. "Here's your Christmas present," she laughed. "I'm happy as I can possibly be."

Rockford
Seminary Days

JANE AND GEORGE grew up. Almost before they knew it they were ready to go to college. George went to a university in the east. Jane went to Rockford Seminary where her sisters had gone, too, before her.

The people of Cedarville thought it was fine that George was going away to study. "He's a smart boy," one man said. "He'll make a doctor like his brother Harry, or maybe a scientist. But I don't understand why Mr. Addams is sending Jane away to school."

"He sent Mary and Alice to college, and see what happened!" another man added. "Both of the girls were married right after they came home from college. What good did a lot of education do them?" Mary had married a minister, Reverend Linn. Alice had married her stepbrother, Dr. Harry Haldeman.

"Girls don't need book learning," others argued. "If they can embroider, sew, cook, and keep house, that's enough. Jane's pretty, and everybody likes her. She'll get married the same as her sisters did. It's a waste of time to have her study."

Mr. Addams did not think the way many people thought about that. "Girls need as much education as boys do," he said. "It helps make them better wives and mothers. Then if they want to teach school or go into business, they can."

The idea of women working made people roll their eyes. "Woman's place is in the home," they thought. "No real lady would ever go into an office to work."

154

Mr. Addams only smiled and sent Jane to Rockford Seminary anyway. Jane had always known she was going to the Seminary. She had always wanted to go, but she was a little afraid to go, too.

She remembered how popular her sisters had been. They had always brought many friends home with them at vacation time. Everyone had said that going to Seminary was great fun.

"I can't laugh and talk and make jokes the way other girls do," she thought. "Maybe they'll think I'm stiff and won't like me. Maybe I won't be able to pass the examinations to get into the school. Father will be ashamed of me."

Jane didn't tell anybody that she was worried, but her father guessed it. "Don't worry, Jane," he told her. "You'll get along all right. You have a good mind. If you get lonely, don't run away and hide. Just be yourself—friendly and kind. Remember how you were afraid to meet the

Jones children when they first moved here to Cedarville, Illinois?"

"But that was different," Jane said. "I was at home then."

There will be other girls there who are away from home for the first time, too. They may be homesick. Make friends with them and cheer them. You'll find your aren't afraid or lonely anymore," Mr. Addams explained.

Jane promised that she'd try his plan, but she hardly thought it would work.

The hours of those first days away from home seemed like weeks. The evenings were the worst time. One day about dusk, Jane came in from a walk around the campus. The lamps in the parlor were lighted. A girl was playing the piano, and several other girls were gathered around her. They seemed to know each other already. It looked cheerful.

Jane wanted to join them, but she was afraid

156

they'd think she was pushing herself in, and that they would snub her. So she stayed back in a dark corner and was miserable. She wished she were home.

Another girl was standing off by herself, too, over by one of the windows. Jane wouldn't have noticed her, but she heard something that sounded like a sniffle. Jane looked up and saw the other girl dab at her eyes.

"She may feel as unhappy as I do," Jane thought. She started to go over to speak. Then her old shyness held her back. Suddenly her father's advice came to her mind. Jane walked quickly to the lonely girl before she lost her courage to speak.

"Don't you wish you could sit down and play the way that girl does and make friends?" Jane asked in a friendly voice. "It almost makes me jealous to watch her. Perhaps you do play, though, and already know everybody."

"Oh, no, I just came. I'm a freshman," the lonely little girl sighed.

"So am I," Jane said eagerly. "My name's Jane Addams, and this is the first time I've been away from home, and I'm so homesick I wish that I were dead."

"Why, I was wishing the same thing," the new girl said laughingly. "My name's Katherine Tanner. I am happy to meet you."

"Katherine, maybe if we go together and join the girls at the piano, they won't notice that we are new. Let's walk over and sing as if we had always lived here. Shall we?"

"I'd love to," Katherine smiled hopefully. The two girls strolled over although their hearts were pounding. They started to sing.

Jane had a surprise, for Katherine had a wonderful voice. In no time at all everybody was begging her to sing this or that favorite song.

Since Jane was the one who had brought

Katherine into the group, the girls thought Jane and Katherine were close friends. Everyone crowded around Jane, too.

They were having so much fun it was supper time before they knew it. When the bell rang, the girls hurried to the dining room together. Everyone walked arm in arm and called each other by their first names as if they were old friends.

Katherine squeezed Jane's hand as she passed her later in the evening. "Thank you so much, Jane, for being so kind. You've made me very happy. I'm all over my homesickness."

Jane was astonished. "Why, I didn't do anything," she said. "But do you know—I'm not homesick any more, either?"

Father's plan had really worked.

From that day on, for the four years Jane was at the Seminary, she was too busy to be lonely. There was always something exciting going on, and she was usually in the middle of it.

160

One afternoon, when Jane was a senior, she stopped by the chapel to watch the students who were trying out for an oratorical contest. The elocution teacher was having them practice going up and down the steps to the platform.

"Don't keep looking down at your feet," she'd scold. "Lift your skirts the least little bit, so you won't trip. Don't walk too fast. Take smaller steps. Now try it over again."

Then she would have them give their speeches. "Don't stand there like a ramrod," she told one girl. "Use your arms to make gestures. Raise your voice. I can't hear you. Now lower it. Let the words roll out like thunder at that place."

The girls did their best, but the teacher looked discouraged. "It isn't that you don't try. You simply haven't prepared good speeches."

"I wouldn't be in those girls' places for anything in the world," Jane whispered to her friend, Ellen Starr, who was sitting next to her.

Jane had barely spoken the words, when the teacher turned around and spoke to Jane. "Jane Addams, you should be in this contest."

Jane moaned, "Oh, I couldn't possibly stand up in front of someone and speak like that."

"You can write a good speech," the teacher went on as if Jane had not said a word. "You are always writing essays and editorials for the school magazine. All you would have to do is to speak what you think instead of writing it." The teacher looked sternly at Jane.

"This is the first time women have been invited to take part in a contest like this. It is an important contest. All the colleges in Illinois are invited to it. We ought to enter it, but we must send someone who can match wits with the men. You're one who can do it. You should be ashamed to say, 'No'."

"Oh, but I can't do it," Jane gasped.

"Yes, you can," Ellen said encouragingly.

162

"You'd do anything for the honor of Rockford Seminary, wouldn't you? You gave the address for the Junior Class Convocation last year without having any trouble."

"But, Ellen, this would be in front of strangers and people who think women shouldn't speak in public. Oh, I just can't."

"Nonsense," Ellen said gaily. "You told us that your father says women must take their place in the affairs of the country. This is your chance to begin."

By this time other girls were crowding around begging Jane to represent the Seminary in the contest. Ellen's last argument settled the matter. Jane would have to try it if it killed her.

Sometimes in the next few weeks she thought it was going to kill her. Jane had no trouble writing the speech nor learning the speech, but speaking it was difficult. Her friends as well as the teacher helped her practice it.

"You have to speak loud enough for people to hear you, Jane. You swallow your words as if you were apologizing for them. Don't you believe in what you are saying?"

"Of course I do," Jane replied. "I wouldn't write something I don't believe."

"Then say it as if you did," the teacher said. "Nobody's going to listen to a timid whisper."

"Try harder, Jane," her friends begged her. "Remember you are speaking for all of us."

Jane practiced and practiced. She tried to think of each thing she had been told to do— hold your head up—throw your arms around— make your voice ring out.

Finally the big day came. Jane and the fellow student who was ready to take Jane's place in case of an accident set out for Galesburg, Illinois. The oratorical contest was to take place there. The whole student body wished them luck and saw them on their way.

The two young women reached Galesburg in good time. They were a little surprised when no one met them at the station to welcome them.

The two girls found the building where the contest was to be held and went directly to the room. Jane walked up to the front of the room exactly as her teacher had coached her.

She stepped boldly up to the platform and introduced herself. Her friends at school would have been proud of her, but they would also have been struck dumb if they had heard what the master of ceremonies said to Jane.

"Young lady, I'm sorry. There has been a mistake somewhere. The contest is over. The prizes have just been awarded."

Jane and her alternate were exactly one day late arriving at the contest.

Jane thought it was a very good joke on herself. "Wasn't I foolish to have worried so much and to have worked so hard for nothing!"

165

The girls at the Seminary were bitterly disappointed. They were sure Jane would have won. When her father heard about it, he assured her that all the work hadn't been "for nothing."

"Some day you'll need every bit of that training and will be glad you had it," he wrote her. Jane couldn't imagine such a time, but at least she was glad she had not turned down her friends.

When summer vacation came again, Jane was proud and happy. She had completed her four years at Rockford Seminary. She had been president of her class, had made good grades, and had made a host of good friends.

"I am really pleased with you, Jane," her stepmother said. "When I first saw you, you were a thin, nervous little girl. Your back hurt you all the time, and you were afraid of your own shadow. Now here we are all of us, riding through the beautiful lake country of Michigan, and you're as well and happy as any of us."

166

Jane's father, her stepmother, her sister Alice, Alice's husband Harry, and her stepbrother George were all taking a trip together.

"I'm proud of you, too, Jennie," her father said. "I know you'll do great things some day." Jane was embarrassed by all these compliments, but they made her happy indeed.

Troubled Times

THAT WAS one of the happiest days of Jane's life. It was one of the saddest, too, for her father suddenly became terribly ill. He died before they could get home.

It didn't seem possible to Jane that the world could go on the same as before. She felt as if she could never smile again. She tried not to be so sad. She told herself everybody had to lose his father some day, but nothing seemed to help her heartache. Her back began to hurt again, too, and it kept on hurting.

"Maybe if I go to work studying again, I'll feel better. I'll go to Philadelphia and study

168

medicine. If I can be a woman doctor, I can do good among the poor in the city. Then I will feel more cheerful."

Jane's back was no better. It became worse than it had ever been. She had to go to bed. Harry and Alice were frantic. They asked many doctors who had special training who might be able to help Dr. Haldeman.

"She'll not live the year out," one of the special doctors said.

Harry wouldn't give up. "Those doctors don't know Jane as well as we do," he said encouragingly to Alice. "She'll get well just to keep you from being so sad."

For a long time Jane didn't get well. Her condition grew worse. It looked as if she were going to die, or at best be a cripple all her life. Her back was strapped to a board, so that she could not move. She lay this way in the hospital for six months.

Alice and her doctor husband never gave up hope. They did everything they could think of to help Jane pass the weary months.

During the bad times Jane kept thinking, "There must be some reason why I keep on living. There must be something in the world I am supposed to do—something that will make life easier or better for someone else. I must try to find out what it is. First, I must get well. No matter how it hurts, I must get up and start walking again as soon as Doctor Harry tells me to try."

The doctors and nurses thought Jane's case was hopeless. "She's suffered too much. She'll never have the courage to try to get on her feet again."

Doctor Harry knew better. After the board was taken away, Jane was put in a plaster cast. Then later a steel ribbed corset took the place of the cast. It held her back straight, and let her get up and move about. Jane walked again!

Wherever Jane went, people said, "Be careful,

Jane. Don't try to lift that. Don't try to walk up the steps. Careful! Careful!"

But Jane kept on doing things. Her back grew stronger. It almost stopped hurting altogether. Now she wanted to try to begin doing something useful. What would it be? She couldn't be a doctor, for she couldn't sit and study a long time. She couldn't be a nurse for her back was still too weak. It seemed there wasn't anything she could do yet.

"While you're getting strong again, Jane," her stepmother said, "why don't we go to Europe? Your father wanted you to travel before you decided what you wanted to do. You can practice your French, Italian, and German while we go through the different countries."

"That's the best thing you could do," Harry assured her. "You can be thinking about your plans for later on, and at the same time you will be getting well again."

Jane went abroad. Three years she lived in the big cities that she had read about—London, Paris, Rome, Berlin. She was not a sad, thin, pale invalid very long. She was a beautiful young lady dressed in velvet and silks who went to the grand balls and the opera.

Jane visited the art galleries and museums and libraries on the Continent of Europe. She studied about the wonderful things she saw and heard, but there was one thing she saw that was not good or wonderful or beautiful. It was ugly.

Back of the grand hotels and behind the opera houses and the art galleries lived the poor people. The only homes they knew were dark, dirty little rooms in dark, dirty buildings. The streets they lived on were so narrow a man could stand in the middle and touch both sides. The sunlight never reached their homes.

"Where do the boys and girls play?" asked Jane. No one answered her. They thought this

172

rich American girl was queer to ask such a strange question.

One cold winter morning in Germany, Jane stood in her pretty, comfortable room in an inn and looked out into the public square. She watched a line of women as they walked back and forth across the square.

Heavy tanks full of boiling hot stuff were fastened to their backs. She could see the steam rising from it in the frosty air. The women were bent low under their heavy loads.

The women were not warmly dressed. Their hands were red with cold. Jane saw one of the women stumble, and the hot stuff splashed on her poor hands. Then she saw that all the women were scarred from burns. She ran from her room and found the innkeeper.

"Who are those women?" she cried. "Where do they go with those tanks on their backs?"

The innkeeper looked at Jane in surprise.

"Why, they work for the brewery. They carry the hot brew to the cooling room across the way."

"Why don't they carry the brew in a cart instead of on their backs?"

The innkeeper shrugged his shoulders. "Ask the owner," he said.

"Take me to him," demanded Jane.

The innkeeper led Jane across the square to the owner of the brewery. He was an important man in the city. Jane asked him why they didn't find a better way to carry the hot beer. "Look at these women!" she cried. "The loads are too heavy. They stumble and are burned. Why don't you have carts and donkeys?"

The man looked at her as if she were crazy. "It costs money to buy carts and donkeys," he replied angrily.

"But what about the women?" she cried. "They're suffering."

The man turned his back. "Dumbhead!" he

175

muttered, and went on about his business, as if she weren't there. She couldn't get him to listen to her or even to look at her.

She went back to the inn. The innkeeper thought she had been foolish, too. "This is none of your affair," he said. "You will get yourself talked about. It has always been done this way. Go on with your art lessons and forget what's none of your business anyhow."

But Jane couldn't forget. Wherever she went, there were the poor people. "Why won't someone do something to help them?" she begged.

Finally one man said angrily, "You think the poor here have a hard time. It is just as bad in your own country."

"But in the United States," said Jane, "people would do something if someone told them and showed them that it was bad."

He laughed at her in scorn. "Well, who's going to tell them so that they will listen. You?"

176

"Yes, I will," said Jane to herself. She went to her hotel and began to pack her trunks. "I'm going home. All the beauty in the world can't make me happy when I know there are people at my back door who are starving, who have never seen the sun on the hills or grass or flowers.

"The people of the United States are kind and generous. I'll go live with the poor in the big cities. Then I'll tell my friends about them. I know they will make things better."

Hull House

Jane Addams came back to America. People said, "Now Jane will live in a fine house and be a fashionable lady."

Jane said, "Now I am going to do what I planned to do when I was a little girl."

She went to Chicago. There, in the very worst part of the city, she found a great big house. It had been a beautiful home in the center of a park, and had been built by a man named Hull. It was still called Hull House, but now it was part of the tenement district. Foreigners from all countries were crowded together there.

Hull House was divided up into many parts

when Jane found it. Upstairs there was a furniture factory. Some of the attic was used for storage. The downstairs was filled with offices and showrooms. It was crowded in between a funeral parlor and a saloon. There was a livery stable where the vegetable gardens had been.

There weren't any trees or grass or flowers within miles. Dirty, rickety buildings walled in filthy, muddy streets. Garbage was thrown out at back doors into open wooden boxes. Millions of flies swarmed over it.

Whole families lived in one room. The crying of children, the angry shouts of men, the shrill voices of tired mothers filled the air.

Jane found the woman who owned Hull House. "I want to rent as much of Hull House as I can have," she said.

The woman looked at Jane. "What in the world can a lovely woman like you want with that place?"

"I'm going to live there," replied Jane. "I want it to be my home as long as I live."

"I don't think you can stand it," said the woman. "It smells so bad. It's so noisy, and the people are so rough."

In the end she rented part of the house to Jane for she saw that Jane knew what she wanted.

Jane and two good friends went to work cleaning the house. They scraped off layers of dirty paint and wallpaper. They sandpapered the floors. Then they scrubbed and polished. Poor Jane's back nearly killed her, but she was so happy, she sang all day long as she worked.

The house was becoming beautiful. Jane Addams and her friends moved into it. They brought their fine rugs and pictures and furniture. Outside was the ugly, smelly city. Inside was a clean, fine home.

Then Jane began to get acquainted with her neighbors. At first people up and down the streets said, "Don't let that Miss Addams in the door. She's up to no good. There's some trick about this. No pretty, rich young woman would move here for nothing."

When she invited them to her house for tea, the women wouldn't come at first. Finally, one of them said, "Let's go see what it looks like in there. We'll keep a sharp watch so she can't trick us into anything."

Jane served tea in her best china and used her finest silver. There were roses on the table and a fire in the fireplace. The room was so pretty the women felt embarrassed. But Jane was friendly and soon they were telling her about Italy, their native country.

They told her, too, how homesick they were sometimes. How glad Jane was that she had gone to Europe, had studied Italian, and knew their country. Now she could understand these neighbors and talk to them.

It made them very happy to find someone who knew their language. They forgot all about the time and stayed and stayed.

They came again the next day and brought their friends and their husbands. How they loved Jane's beautiful home and her pretty things! Best of all they loved her kind heart.

One day Jane was watching some little children in the street. They were making mud pies; that is, they were trying to, but every time they turned out a pie some older boys would jump on it and smash it. Every few minutes, too, the little ones had to run out of the way of the horses and big, lumbering wagons. They were splashed with mud.

"Something must be done about this," said Jane. She remembered how she had made pies in the flour mill and how no one spoiled her fun. She went to the mothers of the neighborhood. "Why don't you keep your children at home?

Aren't you afraid they'll be killed playing in the busy streets?"

"Some of them do get killed," replied the mothers. "Many of them have been crippled. But what can we do? We have to go to work from early morning till late at night. If we leave the children in the house, they play too near the stove and catch fire and are burned to death. That happens, too."

"My little Louie," said one woman, weeping, "fell from the third-story window and was killed while I was gone."

"I tie my little ones to the bed so that they can't get into mischief," said another, "but they cry all day because they get thirsty and hungry."

"The best way is to give them a penny for a roll and lock them out of the house," they all agreed sadly.

"But the big boys take their pennies from them, and then they can't buy anything to eat."

183

"There are always the garbage bins," said one woman sadly.

"But the garbage is full of germs. The children must not eat it," cried Jane.

"Better for them to be hungry than to burn to death or fall from windows," they answered.

"Then let the smallest ones come to my house," said Jane. "I'll take care of them while you are at work."

"They'll break your nice things," said the women. But oh, how glad they were to have their children safe and warm and fed!

More and more women left their little ones in Jane's care. She rented another room and made a playroom for them. She had a big sand pile built where they could make all the mud pies they wanted and no one was allowed to touch them. She bought picture books and storybooks and read to them.

Soon the older children, the boys who had

jumped on the pies, begged to be allowed to play there, too. Jane took them all in. She bought tools and games and more grown-up books.

"I need more room and more money and many helpers," said Jane. She went to her friends, rich and poor. She told them about these neighbors of hers, and about their needs. Now her training for the oratorical contest at Rockford served a good purpose. Jane Addams spoke out clearly in order that people could hear her. There was no timid whisper in her voice. She let it roll out, for she believed in what she was saying. For her friends who needed help, she would ask help from those friends who had the wealth and health to share.

Then just what Jane had told the man in Europe would happen did happen. The people of the United States began to do something when they heard about the poor people. The woman who owned Hull House gave it to Jane rent-free, the whole house. Another woman gave money for a great big nursery. A man who owned a block of tenement buildings gave them to her. "Fix them up, tear them down, do what you want," he said.

Young women and young men from good homes came and lived at Hull House and helped take care of Jane's neighbors. They looked after the little children, they scrubbed floors, washed windows, cooked for Jane's guests, planned parties and club meetings. They helped keep Hull House bright and clean, for Jane couldn't begin to do everything now. But she managed all of it, and always met her guests at the front door herself.

Young folks and old folks filled Hull House to overflowing. People gave Jane still more money to buy more space. She had a gymnasium built and club rooms added.

"This still is not enough," said Jane. "My

neighbors have to work too long and don't make enough to live on. Fathers and mothers leave their children early in the morning and return at night. They work in attics with no fresh air. Women faint from the heat in the summer and shiver with cold in the winter. They earn maybe a dollar a day.

"Even little children work. They are crowded into factories that are firetraps. They work at least twelve hours a day and don't earn a dollar. Children need to play in the fresh air."

Jane thought of the wonderful times she had had playing upon the meadows and along the streams at Cedarville.

"We must make laws that won't allow little children to work in factories. The working places of all people must be light, airy, and safe. Working hours must be shorter so that men will have more time to enjoy their families. Men must be paid more so that they can buy things they need."

188

The people of the United States listened to Jane Addams. They made more just and kindly laws. The city became a better place to live.

All these wonderful things that Jane brought about did not happen overnight. They took years and years of careful planning and hard work. To accomplish these things took the kind of courage and patience that Jane showed she had when she lay suffering in the hospital and still was determined to get up and walk again.

Jane Addams spent a whole lifetime making these things happen. With the help of her friends she had opened Hull House in 1889. The work of Jane Addams at Hull House was studied and discussed far from Chicago, Illinois, and the United States. Governments and organizations throughout the world followed the results of her efforts.

Miss Addams worked to let the world know how the living conditions and working conditions should be improved. She gave lectures and wrote books to give her message to everyone who was interested. Because she knew the truth of the material about which she was writing, her books were useful to the readers.

She was known as one of the first great social workers, and many young people have studied social service to try to continue the kind of work she began.

To tell the world of her personal experiences, Jane Addams wrote two very interesting books, *Twenty Years at Hull House* and *The Second Twenty Years.* Jane's teachers had thought she could both write well and speak well. She used both of these talents to help other people.

After Jane Addams had spent so much of her time trying to improve the conditions in the cities around her, she also became interested in helping promote peace in the world. From the time of its founding until Miss Addams' death, she served as president of the Women's International League for Peace and Freedom.

The year 1931 brought some of the greatest honors to Jane Addams. She was chosen as first among the "twelve greatest living women of America" by a committee of men for a popular magazine for women. Other lists of outstanding women included Jane Addams' name. Universities honored her with special awards.

The greatest honor of the year was her selection as the winner of the Nobel Peace Prize. The minister from the United States who accepted her award on December 10, in Oslo, Norway, said of Jane Addams, ". . . In Jane Addams there are assembled all the best womanly attributes which shall help us to establish peace in the world. . . ."

Jane Addams' death on May 21, 1935, did not bring to an end her work at Hull House. Almost immediately after her death the "Jane

Addams Memorial Fund" was established to continue the support of her work at the settlement. Other memorials have been created to keep alive the memory of Jane Addams' great unselfish personality.

The people of the world asked, "Who would have thought that one little girl with a crooked back could do so much?"

"We would," replied her friends of Cedarville. "We knew her."

"We would," replied her friends of Hull House. "We knew her heart. It was pure gold."

Jane had found the gold at the end of the rainbow after all. She had stored it in her heart, and had shared it with those who needed it most.

More About This Book

WHEN JANE ADDAMS LIVED

1860   JANE ADDAMS WAS BORN IN CEDARVILLE, ILLI-NOIS, SEPTEMBER 6.

There were thirty-three states in the Union.

James Buchanan was President.

The population of the country was about 31,440,000.

1860–1876   JANE LIVED IN CEDARVILLE WITH HER FAMILY, STUDIED AT HOME, AND ATTENDED SCHOOL.

The War between the States was fought, 1861-1865.

Abraham Lincoln was President, 1861-1865.

The United States purchased Alaska, 1867.

Alexander G. Bell invented the telephone, 1876.

1877   JANE ENTERED ROCKFORD SEMINARY.

Bicycles were first made in this country, 1878.

Thomas Edison invented the phonograph, 1878, and the electric light bulb, 1879.

1881   JANE ADDAMS GRADUATED FROM ROCKFORD SEMINARY.

Clara Barton founded the American Red Cross, 1881.

The first electric street railway in the United States was operated, 1885.

The Statue of Liberty was dedicated, 1886.

1889   JANE ADDAMS OPENED HULL HOUSE IN CHICAGO, ILLINOIS.

The Spanish-American War was fought, 1898.

Wilbur and Orville Wright flew the first heavier-than-air aircraft, 1903.

1915   JANE ADDAMS BEGAN WORK FOR WOMEN'S INTERNATIONAL LEAGUE FOR PEACE.

The United States entered World War I, 1917.

Great depression started in the United States, 1929-1931.

1931   JANE ADDAMS WAS AWARDED THE NOBEL PEACE PRIZE.

Amelia Earhart flew a small airplane across the Atlantic Ocean alone, 1932.

Wiley Post flew a small airplane around the world, 1933.

1935 JANE ADDAMS DIED, MAY 21.

There were forty-eight states in the Union.

Franklin D. Roosevelt was President.

The population of the country was about 127,190,000.

DO YOU REMEMBER?

1. Where did Jane Addams live and how old was she when the story opened?

2. What dangerous game did Jane show her friends at the sawmill?

3. How did she use part of the flour mill for a playhouse?

4. Why was she a little lame girl?

5. Why did the Jones family move to Cedarville?

6. Who made a real playhouse in the Addams' yard for Jane?

7. Why was Jane not able to attend regular school all of the time?

8. Why did Alice Addams decide not to go to boarding school?

9. How did some boys show cruelty to Jane one Sunday morning?

10. Why did Alice want Jane to have a new coat for Sunday use?

11. Who was George Haldeman?

12. How did Jane show bravery on the nut-hunting trip with George and his friends?

13. What were some of the interesting adventures George and Jane had together?

14. Where did Jane Addams attend school after she left Cedarville?

15. What made her want to try to improve the living conditions in tenement districts?

16. What was the name of the social settlement house she opened in Chicago, Illinois?

IT'S FUN TO LOOK UP THESE THINGS

1. Where are volunteer fire departments still found today?

2. How old are kittens when their eyes open?

3. How can one recognize a copperhead snake?

4. Why are bayberry candles especially valued?

5. For what purpose and where are oratorical contests held?

6. What were some of the achievements of Ellen Starr?

7. By what name is Rockford Seminary now known?

8. What was the first name of the Women's International League for Peace and Freedom?

9. How many awards did Miss Addams receive in 1931?

INTERESTING THINGS YOU CAN DO

1. Gather information on the settlement houses or other social work which is being done in your community or in a large nearby city. Ask your teacher if you may give a report on your findings to your classmates.

2. Learn who established the Nobel Prize, what it is, and to whom it is awarded. Make a chart of the Americans who have won it, when they won it, and why they won.

3. Find pictures of Hull House at the time it first became a settlement house and as it appears today. Arrange the pictures on the poster board of your classroom.

4. Plan an imaginary trip to the memorials which now honor Jane Addams.

OTHER BOOKS YOU MAY ENJOY READING

Clara Barton: Girl Nurse, Augusta Stevenson. Trade and School Editions, Bobbs-Merrill.

Famous Women of America, William Oliver Stevens. Dodd.

Juliette Low: Girl Scout, Helen Boyd Higgins. Trade and School Editions, Bobbs-Merrill.

Lincoln and Douglas, Regina Z. Kelly. Trade Edition, Random House. School Edition, Hale.

Story of Albert Schweitzer, The, Anita Daniel. Trade Edition, Random House. School Edition, Hale.

Yesterday in America, Harold B. Clifford. American Book Company.

INTERESTING WORDS IN THIS BOOK

astonishment (ăs tŏn'ĭsh mĕnt) : extreme surprise

brewery (brōō'ēr ĭ) : place in which beer and other malted liquors are made

coaxing (kōks'ĭng) : trying to gain with soft words or flattery

college (kŏl'ĕj) : educational institution above the high school level, which gives degrees to its students upon completion of certain courses

continent (kŏn'tĭ nĕnt) : mainland of Europe as distinguished from the British Isles.

drenching (drĕnch'ĭng) : complete wetting, soaking

embarrassed (ĕm băr'ăst) : worried, confused

flocking (flŏk'ĭng) : moving together

flurry (flûr'ĭ) : sudden movement of air which may produce a shower of rain or snow

foreigner (fŏr'ĭn ẽr) : person from some other country or nation

foreman (fōr'măn) : man in charge of a group of workmen

gallery (găl'ẽr ĭ) : building or room for showing works of art or the like

glittered (glĭt'ẽrd) : sparkled

graduated (grăd'u̇ āt'ĕd) : having completed a given course of studies and receiving a diploma

gymnasium (jĭm nā'zĭ ŭm) : building or room for physical exercise

invalid (ĭn'va̍ lĭd) : person who is weak or sick

livery stable (lĭv'ẽr ĭ) : stable where horses and vehicles are kept for hire or cared for

museum (mu̇ zē'ŭm) : building in which objects of interest, especially of scientific or artistic interest, are kept and displayed

pranced (prănst) : moved with springing steps

pried (prīd) : raised or pulled apart

rickety (rĭk'ĕ tĭ) : shaky, weak

saloon (så loon') : shop where liquors are sold

seamstress (sēm'strĕs) : woman who does sewing

seminary (sĕm'ĭ nĕr'ĭ) : private school

sheepish (shēp'ĭsh) : bashful or timid

shriek (shrēk) : cry out sharply

slum (slŭm) : dirty, densely populated street or district of a town or city

snarling (snärl'ing) : making a growling noise

squirmed (skwûrmd) : twisted about like a snake; wriggle; writhe

stanza (stăn'zå) : group of lines or verses, varying in number, forming a unit or section of a poem or song

sulked (sŭlkt) : acted in a bad mood

tenement house (ten'ĕ mĕnt) : large building having many sets of rooms, each set occupied by a family, used commonly to describe buildings occupied by families of low income

tinsel (tĭn'sĕl) : strips of glittering, metallic material used as an inexpensive trimming